151 Akbar-Birbal STORIES

MANOJ PUBLICATIONS

151 Akbar-Birbal Stories

Publisher:
MANOJ PUBLICATIONS
761, Main Road, Burari, Delhi-110084
Ph. : 27611116, 27611349
Fax : 27611546, Mob. : 9868112194
email : info@manojpublications.com
For online shopping visit our website: **www.manojpublications.com**

Showroom :
1583-84, Dariba Kalan, Chandni Chowk, Delhi-110006
Ph. : 23262174, 23268216
Mobile : 9818753569

ISBN : 978-81-310-1948-1

CONTENTS

1. *Akbar Meets Birbal*

While hunting in a forest, Akbar lost his way. A man named Mahesh Das helped him find his way out. Akbar was pleased. He gave Mahesh his gold ring and invited him to his palace. Some days later, Mahesh went to Akbar's palace but the guard did not let him in. Mahesh showed him Akbar's ring. The guard said, "I'll let you in. But you should give me half of what the emperor gives you." Mahesh agreed. When Akbar saw Mahesh, he said, "What's your wish, young man?" Mahesh replied, "Your Majesty, please beat me fifty times with a stick." Akbar ordered his soldier to beat Mahesh. After receiving twenty-five beatings, Mahesh said, "Stop! Now call the guard and beat him twenty-five times. He wanted half of what the emperor gave me." The guard was called in. He was shocked. Impressed with Mahesh's intelligence, Akbar made him his chief minister.

2. *Birbal's Daughter in the Royal Court*

Birbal had a seven-year-old daughter. One day, she said to him, "Father, I've heard so much about Emperor Akbar's court. Will you take me there with you tomorrow?" Birbal said, "Yes dear, we shall go there tomorrow morning." Next day, they went to the royal court. When Akbar saw Birbal's daughter, he asked, "Do you know Persian?" The child replied, "Your Majesty, a little less and a little more." Akbar turned to Birbal and said, "I did not understand what your daughter said. Can you please explain?" Birbal said, "Your Majesty, she means that she knows Persian a little less than those who know it well and a little more than those who don't know Persian." Akbar was impressed with the child's intelligence. He chuckled in amusement and said, "Birbal, your daughter is indeed as smart as you. You must be so proud of her!"

3. *Boy in the Mango Orchard*

One evening, Akbar was strolling in his mango orchard. Suddenly, an arrow whizzed by. Akbar ordered, "Soldiers! Find the person who tried to kill me!" Soon, the soldiers fetched the boy who had shot the arrow. Akbar asked, "Why did you try to kill me?" The boy said, "Your Majesty, I was aiming at a ripe mango but the arrow almost hit you instead." Akbar angrily ordered, "Soldiers! Kill the boy in the same way he tried to kill me." The soldiers tied the boy to a tree near by. When they were about to shoot the boy, Birbal said, "Your Majesty, in order to kill the boy in the same way, you should aim for a mango. The arrow should miss the mango and hit the boy instead." Akbar said, "If the boy had wanted to kill me, he would have aimed at me, not at the mango. Let him go!"

4. Akbar's Ring in the Well

Once, Akbar went hunting with his courtiers. Birbal was also with him. When some time had passed, Akbar felt thirsty. Soon, they spotted a well. Akbar got off his horse and peeped into it. The well was dry. He was about to turn away, when one of his rings slipped from his finger and into the well. Birbal saw this. He left the place, only to return after some time with some fresh cow-dung. He threw the dung on the ring. Then he tied a long string to a stone and threw it on the cow-dung. Then they all went hunting. Before sunset, Birbal asked Akbar to stop by the well. Then he pulled the string. Along with it came the stone, which had stuck to the dried cow-dung. Underneath it all there was Akbar's ring, set in the dung. Akbar praised Birbal and gave him precious gifts.

5. The Tub of Milk

One morning, Akbar and Birbal were strolling in the royal garden. Akbar said, "My subjects always obey me." Birbal replied, "But they also fear you, Your Majesty!" Akbar said, "Unbelievable! Prove it." Birbal said, "Your Majesty, announce that the subjects should pour a pot of milk into a tub placed in the royal courtyard." Akbar did so and added that he was going on a hunting trip for a few days. When he returned, he found that the tub was full of water. Birbal said, "Your Majesty, announce that the subjects should fill the tub with milk and say that you will check the tub once you are back after hunting." Akbar did so and left for his hunting trip once again. When he returned, he saw that the tub was full of milk. Birbal asked Akbar, "Now do you believe that your subjects obey you out of fear, Your Majesty?" Akbar nodded and smiled.

6. *Three Witty Answers*

Akbar always praised Birbal for his wit and intelligence. Because of this, one courtier was very jealous of Birbal. He told Akbar, "I have three questions for Birbal. If he answers correctly, I will accept that he is intelligent." Akbar agreed. The jealous courtier asked Birbal, "Where is the centre of the Earth?" Birbal said, "My home is the centre of the Earth." The courtier asked, "How many stars are there in the sky?" Birbal brought a sheep and replied, "The number of stars equals the number of hair on this sheep. Count them yourself." Taken aback by the prompt replies, the jealous courtier asked, "How many men and women are there in the world?" To this, Birbal replied, "The exact number can be reached only if all the jealous people of the world, including you, are left out." Akbar chuckled in amusement and ordered the jealous courtier to leave at once.

7. *Thief in the Merchant's Mansion*

Birbal was the favourite not only of Akbar, but also of his subjects, because he would solve their problems quickly. Once, a merchant came to him. A theft had taken place and he thought one of his five servants must be the thief. "Let's go to your house," said Birbal. On the way, he broke five twigs from a tree. On reaching the merchant's mansion, Birbal gave the servants a twig each. He said, "The thief's twig will grow by three inches," and left. The servant who had stolen the merchant's valuables hurriedly cut his twig by three inches. Next day, Birbal asked the servants to bring the twigs he had given them. One of the servants held out a twig that was smaller by three inches. Birbal said to the merchant, "Here's your thief. He cut the twig fearing that it might grow." The merchant thanked Birbal and punished the thief.

8. *The Tunnel to Heaven*

Some courtiers, who were jealous of Birbal, decided to get rid of him with the royal barber's help. They promised the barber a lot of money. The wicked barber agreed. He told Akbar, "Your Majesty, a magician is in town. He can perform a ritual to help you know about the well-being of your ancestors." Akbar asked, "How?" The barber said, "Set up a funeral pyre and gift an intelligent person to the gods." Akbar asked Birbal to do the job. Birbal said, "Please give me a few days off. I want to make arrangements for my family before I leave." During this time, Birbal dug a tunnel from the place of the funeral pyre to his home. On the day of the ritual, Birbal escaped through the tunnel and went home. Months later, he visited Akbar and said, "Your ancestors are fine, but they need a barber." The barber realised his mistake and asked for Birbal's forgiveness.

9. *The Honest 'Hens'*

Akbar loved to play pranks on his courtiers. One day, it was Birbal's turn. Before Birbal reached the court, Akbar gave an egg to each courtier and said, "Hide it in the royal courtyard until I ask you for it." When Birbal arrived, Akbar told him, "Those who bring me eggs from the royal courtyard will be declared my honest courtiers." One by one, all the courtiers left the court and returned with the egg Akbar had given each of them earlier. In the end, it was Birbal's turn. He went to the courtyard and couldn't find any egg and realised that Akbar was playing a prank. He entered the court crowing like a rooster. When Akbar asked for the egg, Birbal said, "Your Majesty, I am a rooster. Hens lay eggs, not roosters." At this, everyone in the court burst out laughing. Once again, Akbar was pleased with Birbal's wit.

10. *Birbal's Choice*

Akbar held Birbal's opinion above everyone else's. When in a leisurely mood, he would chat with Birbal. Once, he asked Birbal, "If you had to choose between justice and money, which would you prefer?" Birbal replied, "Your Majesty, without a thought, I would go for the money." Akbar was taken aback. He said, "Take your time, Birbal. Think before you reply." Birbal said, "My answer will still be the same, Your Majesty." Akbar was upset. He said, "I thought you are different. But you are just as greedy as everyone else. How could you choose the money instead of justice?" Birbal said, "Your Majesty, you are a kind and just ruler. Your subjects can rest assured that they will have justice in your kingdom. But they are poor and do not have enough money. That is why I chose money." Pleased with Birbal, Akbar gave him a thousand gold coins.

11. *Akbar and the Saint*

Akbar woke up in a foul mood one day. Nothing anyone said or did seemed to please him. To top it all, Birbal also played a prank on him. Akbar was furious and he ordered Birbal to leave the city at once. Birbal was very sad. He packed his bags and left. Akbar started missing Birbal. But he couldn't do anything since he knew Birbal would have followed his order and left the city. After a few days, a saint decided to visit Akbar's palace. He had two disciples with him, who said, "Our master can solve all problems and perform miracles." Akbar asked the saint many difficult questions and the saint answered them all. Then Akbar said, "If you can perform miracles, make Birbal appear before us." Immediately, the saint tore off his beard and wig, and there stood Birbal. Akbar was happy and he welcomed Birbal with open arms.

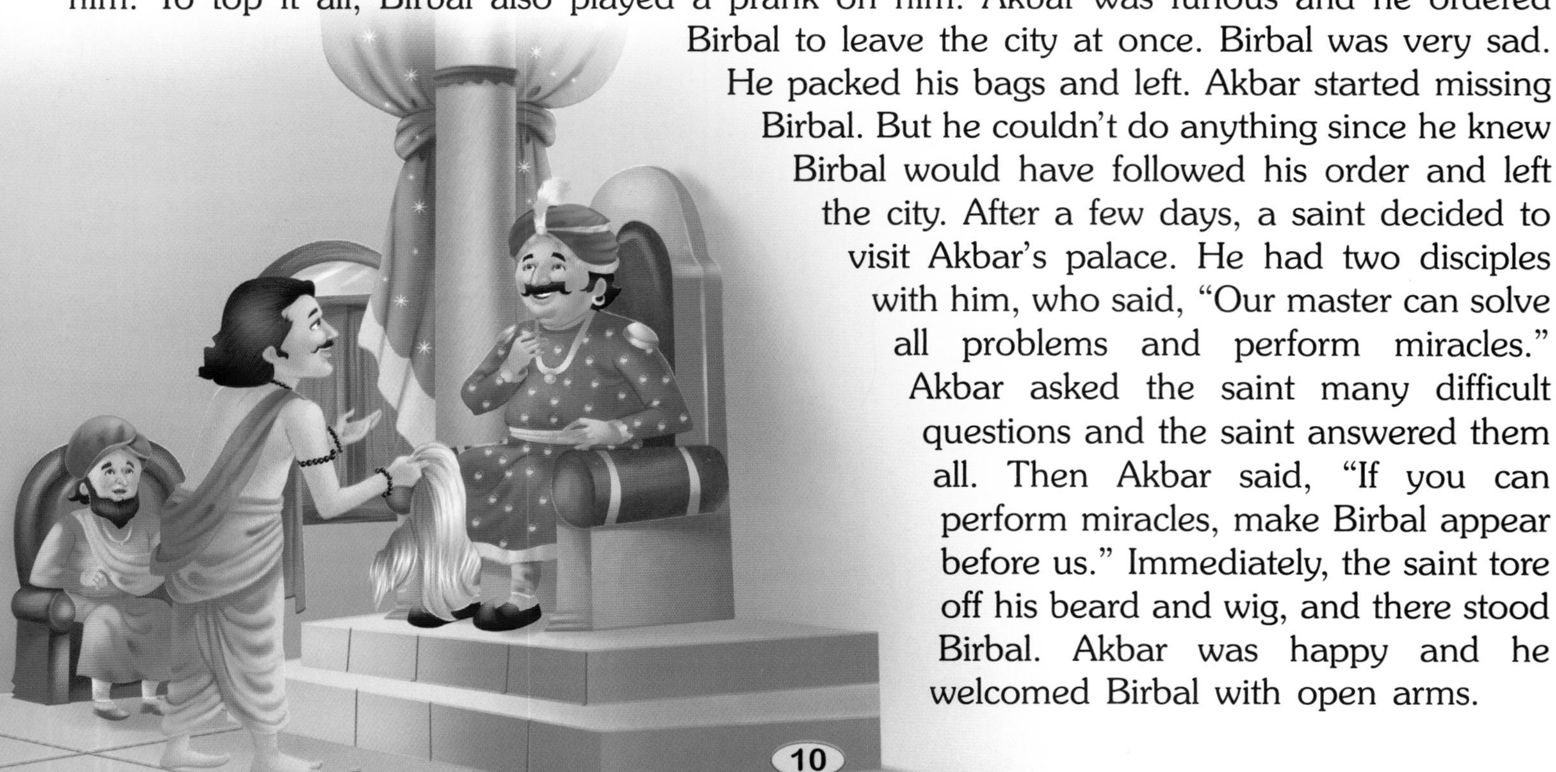

12. *Birbal Passes the Test*

One day, Akbar wanted to test Birbal's wit. When Birbal entered court, Akbar said, "I have a few questions for you." Birbal settled into his seat and said, "I'm ready, Your Majesty. Let's begin." Akbar said, "The sun and the moon are high up in the sky. Is there anything they cannot see?" Birbal said, "Yes, Your Majesty; they cannot see darkness." Akbar said, "What is the difference between truth and lies?" Birbal replied, "It is the difference between our eyes and ears. Because what we see is truth but what we hear is usually false." Akbar was pleased. Then he drew a line on the floor and said, "Birbal, shorten this line without touching it." Birbal drew a longer line next to it and said, "There, Your Majesty; I've done it." Akbar was satisfied with all of Birbal's answers and showered Birbal with many gifts.

13. *Birbal and the Brahmin*

Once, a Brahmin named Sevaram came to visit Birbal. He did not have much wealth and lived a simple life. He was sad. He said to Birbal, "I come from a family of scholars. I do not want wealth. Everyone addressed my ancestors as 'Panditji'. I want everyone to address me the same way." Birbal said, "That is easy. Just ask everyone not to address you by that name." A few children lived near Sevaram's house. Birbal told the children that Severam will not like it if they addressed Sevaram as 'Panditji'. When they called him 'Panditji', Sevaram would shout, "Don't call me 'Panditji'." This made the children laugh. They went around telling everyone that they should call him 'Panditji'. Soon, everyone in the city began addressing Sevaram as 'Panditji'. After some time, he stopped scolding the children when they addressed him as 'Panditji'. Now he was a happy man.

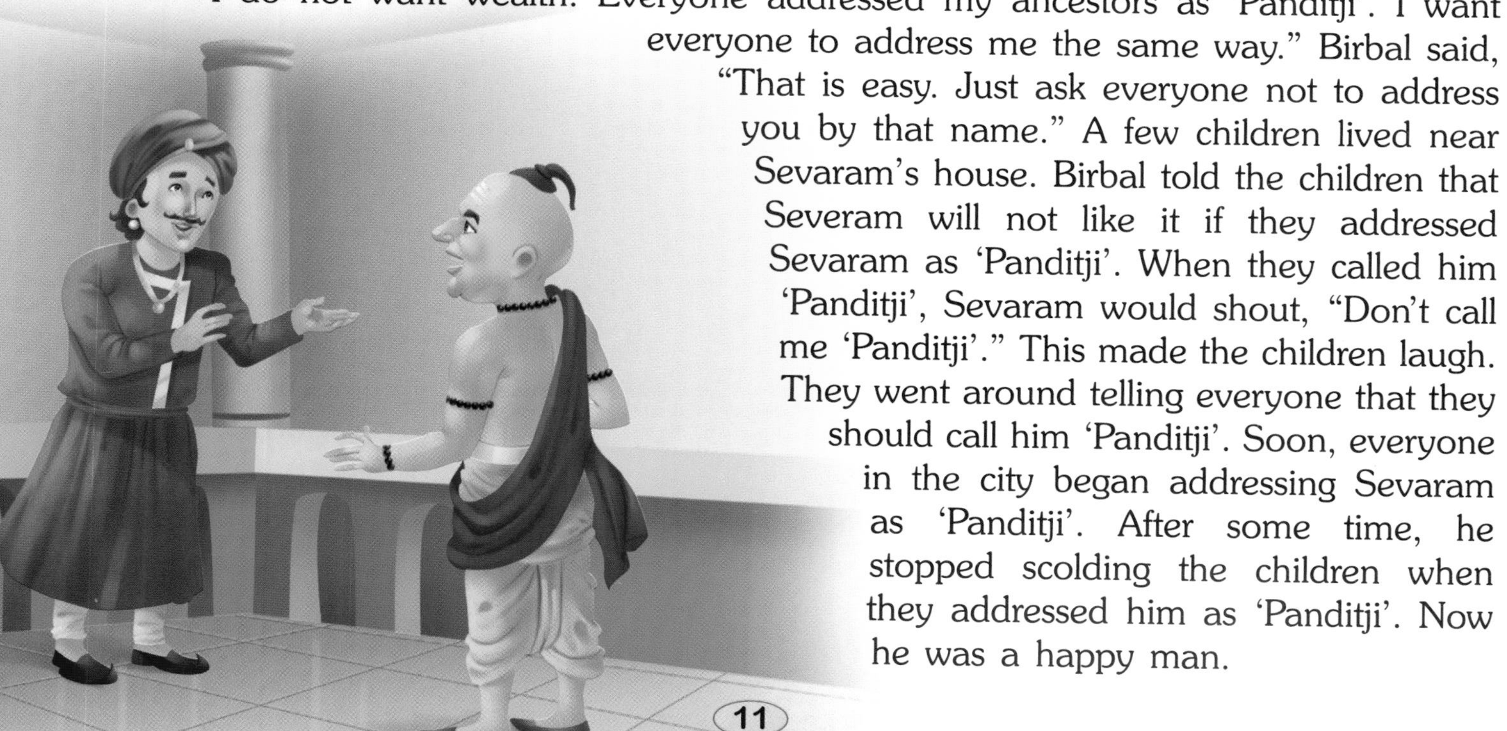

14. *Akbar's Dream*

Birbal was not just blessed with a clever mind. He also had a different way of looking at every situation. He had a positive attitude. One morning, Akbar was upset with a dream he had. He sent for many renowned astrologers. When they all reached his palace, he asked them to interpret the dream he had the previous night. "I dreamt that all my teeth, except one, had fallen out. What does that mean?" The astrologers made some calculations and arrived at a conclusion. All of them were of the opinion that Akbar's relatives would all die before he. Akbar was not happy to hear this. He sent them all away. Birbal saw that Akbar was sad and things were getting worse. He said, "Cheer up, Your Majesty! The dream means that you will live longer than all your relatives!" Akbar smiled and nodded. Once again, Birbal had made his day.

15. *The Tradesman and his Servant*

One day, two men entered the royal courtroom. One of them said, "Birbal, please help me. My name is Aamir. I am a tradesman. I had gone abroad after entrusting my servant with my property. But when I returned, I saw that my servant has stolen all my money and is using my name. He also refuses to recognise me." The second man said, "No, Your Majesty! I am Aamir. But this man insists that I am his servant." Birbal said, "I can read your minds." Birbal stood there, looking at the men for a while. Then he ordered the guard, "Off with the thief's head!" The guard did not know who the servant was, but he walked towards the men. Just when he neared them, the thief ran to Akbar and begged for mercy. Birbal said, "The thief got scared when I lied that I could read minds." Akbar smiled.

16. *Birbal and the Flatterer*

Birbal and his daughter were in the spice market, when a man came to him and said, "Are you the famous Birbal from Akbar's court?" Birbal said, "Yes, I am." The man said, "I have heard great tales about your generosity. I have come all the way from a distant city just to meet you. Throughout my journey, I met people who said you are very kind and fulfil everyone's wish." Birbal understood that the man was flattering him. Birbal said, "I feel great after meeting you, dear gentleman. Will you be going home by the same route?" The man replied, "Yes, sir." Birbal said, "Please tell everyone on your way back that the tales of my generosity are untrue." The man understood that Birbal would not be influenced by his sweet talk. Sometimes, people try to fool others with flattery. But Birbal knew how to deal with such people.

17. *The Copycat Horse*

There was a wealthy man in Akbar's kingdom. He bought a handsome horse. But within a few months the horse started limping. The man called many veterinarians to examine his horse but they could not cure it since there was no sprain, fracture or wound. The man thought, 'Only Birbal can cure my horse.' After listening to the man, Birbal asked him, "Have you changed anything in your horse's routine or diet recently?" The man said, "Yes, I have changed the horse's trainer." "Does your horse like his trainer?" asked Birbal. "Yes, he does. He follows all his commands," said the man. Birbal asked, "Does the trainer limp?" The man's eyes brightened and he replied, "Yes! He does." Birbal said, "Many a time, we try to copy every action of those we admire. Your horse is trying to be like his trainer." The man changed the horse's trainer. Soon, his horse stopped limping.

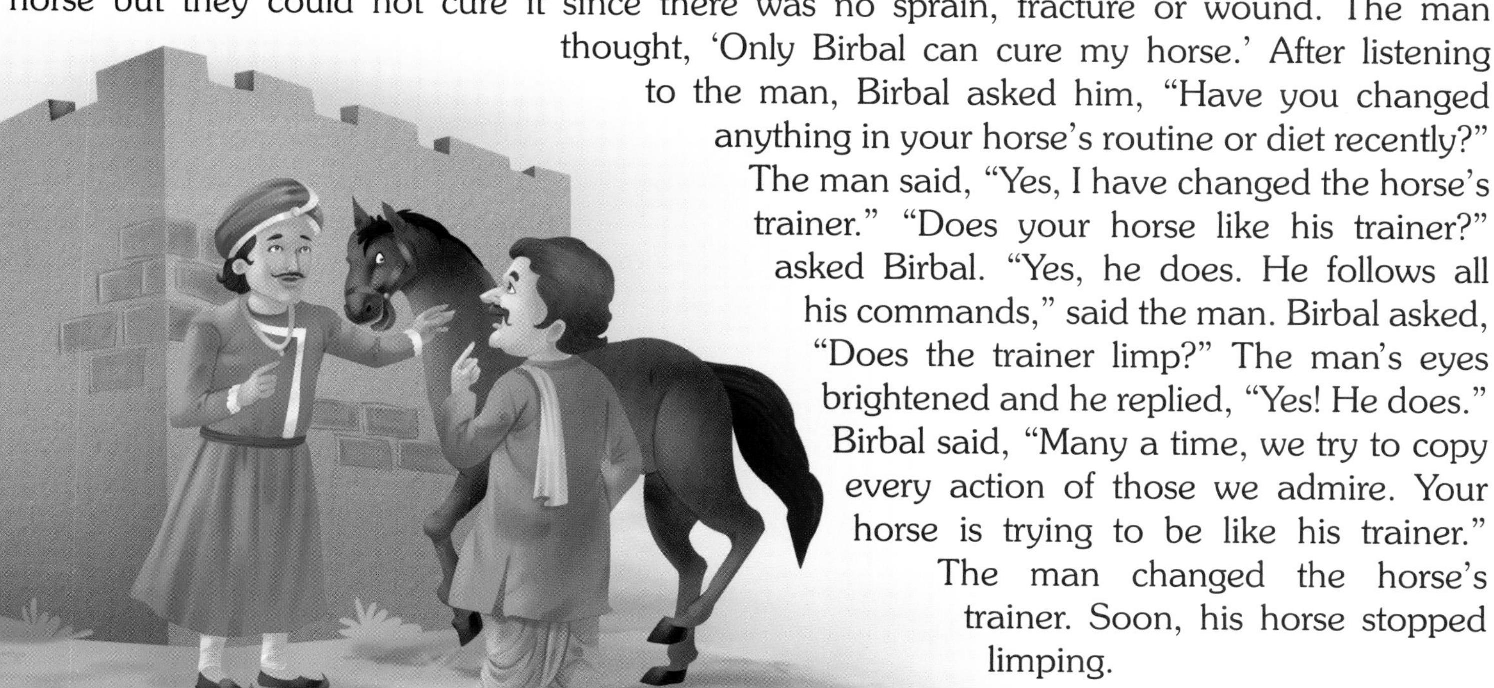

18. *Birbal Becomes a Cobbler*

One day, Akbar wanted to know how many blind people lived in his kingdom. He asked Birbal about it and Birbal replied, "Your Majesty, please grant me a week's holiday to find the answer to your question." Akbar granted him leave. The next day onwards, Birbal stopped going to the royal court. Instead, he began mending shoes in the local market. People were surprised to see him there. Everyone would stop by and ask, "Birbal, what are you doing here?" Soon, Akbar went to the market and asked Birbal the same question, but Birbal did not respond. After a week, Birbal went back to the royal court with a long list of blind people. Akbar was angry when he saw his name on the list. Birbal explained, "Your Majesty, like the rest, you saw me mending shoes, yet you asked me what I was doing." Akbar laughed heartily at Birbal's act.

19. *The Emperor's Invitation*

There are people who think wealth is necessary to earn respect. Akbar thought so, too. He asked Birbal, "Is it possible for a man to be poor and yet earn respect?" "Yes, Your Majesty," replied Birbal. Akbar said, "If this is possible, find such a person and bring him to me." Birbal went out on the streets. He had not gone far when he saw a beggar with tattered clothes. He was old and walked with the help of a stick. He had not earned a penny since morning. He had not eaten for days and was weak. Birbal took the beggar by his hand and led him into the palace. When Akbar saw the beggar, he asked, "This man is poor, but how does he command respect?" Birbal replied, "This man does not own a penny. Yet he has been invited by the greatest Emperor — and that is you, Your Majesty!"

20. *Birbal's Painting*

One day, Akbar said to Birbal, "You can solve any problem in a jiffy. You must be good at painting too." Birbal said, "No, Your Majesty! I can't even hold a painting brush." Akbar angrily said, "I am an art-lover. You cannot say 'no' to me. I want you to imagine and create a painting. It should be ready within a week." Birbal did not know what to do, but he had no choice. After a week, Birbal walked in with his painting. Akbar was furious when he saw it. He said, "Birbal! There are just a few patches of blue and white. What kind of a painting is this?" Birbal replied, "Your Majesty! You asked me to imagine. I imagined a cow and some grass. The cow ate the grass and went to her shed. All that remains is the sky and the clouds." Akbar had a hearty laugh.

21. *Simple but Difficult*

Akbar would ask Birbal the trickiest of questions to test his intelligence. One day, he said to Birbal, "I have a simple question for you, Birbal. How many bangles does your wife wear?" Birbal said, "Your Majesty, I do not know." Akbar said, "She serves you food every day. Yet, you don't know." Birbal replied, "I can explain that in the garden downstairs, Your Majesty." Akbar said, "Come, let's go," and they both climbed down the stairs and entered the royal garden. When Akbar wanted to know the reason why Birbal didn't know the answer, Birbal said, "Your Majesty, can you tell me the number of stairs we climbed down just now?" Akbar said, "No, I don't know." Birbal said, "Your Majesty, we climb up and down the same flight of stairs every day." Akbar smiled and said, "I've understood that one shouldn't ask questions that one doesn't have answers for."

22. *The Blind Saint*

Once, a couple went to visit a saint with their niece. The saint was blind. But as soon as the niece saw the saint, she cried, "This man killed my parents. Punish him!" The saint said, "How can a blind man like me kill someone? Take this girl away." The couple came home but they felt their niece was telling the truth. So they went to Birbal and told him all about the matter. Birbal invited the saint to Akbar's court. When the saint entered, Birbal drew out his sword and walked towards him. The saint immediately drew out a sword and began defending himself. Everyone in the court was shocked to see this. Then Birbal turned to Akbar and said, "Your Majesty, this man is not blind. I doubt whether he is a saint." Akbar praised Birbal's intelligence and punished the wicked man who was posing as a saint.

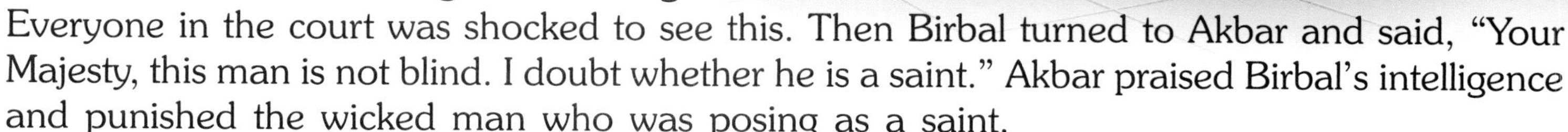

23. *The Marriage Procession*

Akbar and Birbal shared a close relationship. This made the courtiers jealous of Birbal. One of them said to Akbar, "Your Majesty, why do you listen to Birbal and ignore our suggestions?" Akbar thought he should prove that Birbal was better than the rest. A marriage procession was passing by and Akbar asked the jealous courtier to find out whose marriage it was. Akbar asked Birbal to do the same. The jealous courtier ran fast and reached the marriage procession. He returned with the same speed. Soon, Birbal returned too. Akbar asked the courtier, "Where is the procession headed?" "I don't know, Your Majesty," replied the courtier. But Birbal answered, "They are going to Allahabad, Your Majesty." Akbar turned to the jealous courtier and said, "Being smart requires doing more than what is asked. Now, do you understand why Birbal is my favourite?" The jealous courtier hung his head in shame.

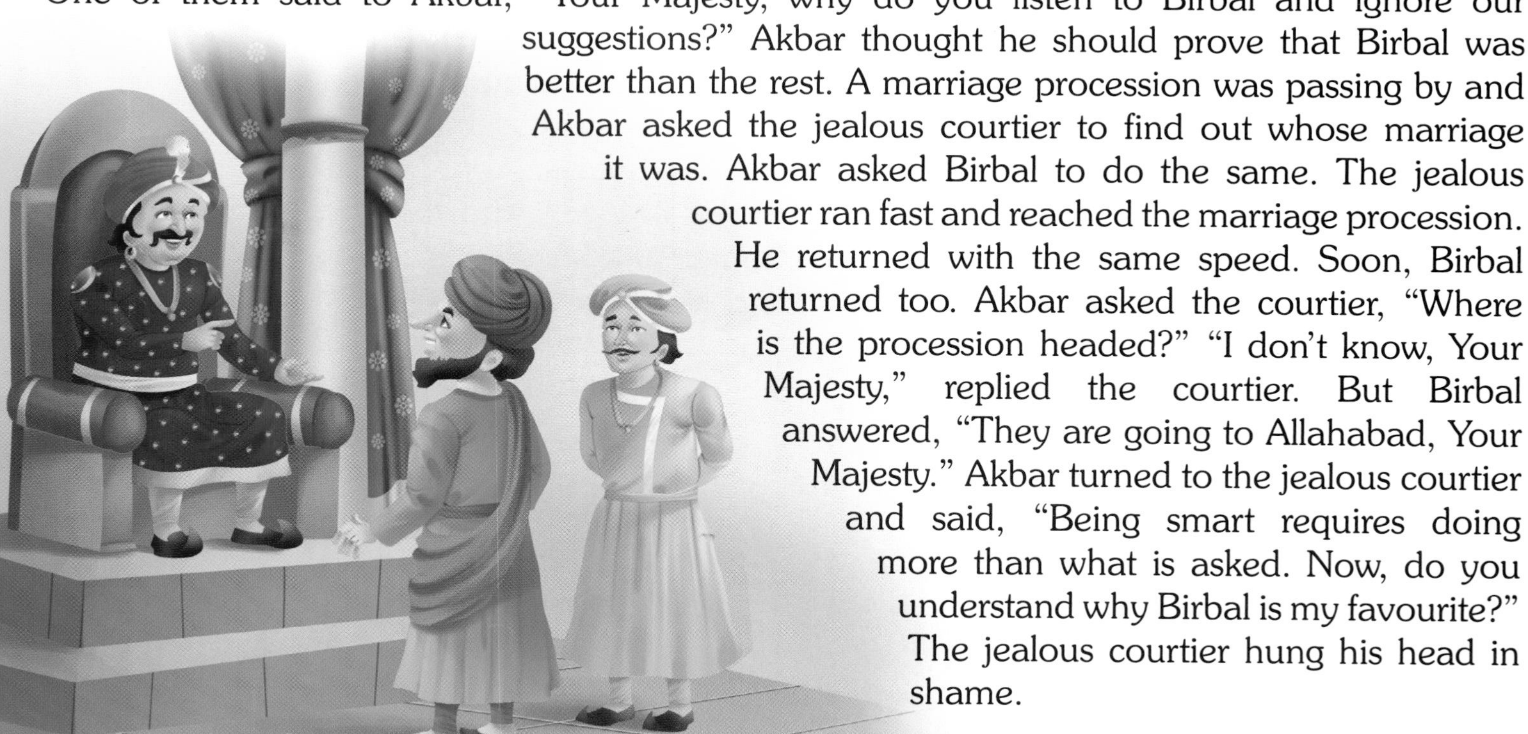

24. *The Good Gardener*

One morning, Akbar was walking in the garden. He was deep in thought when he stumbled against a small rock and hurt his foot. Angrily, he sent for the royal gardener. He told the gardener, "I hurt my foot because of you. You shall be sentenced to death tomorrow." The gardener's pleas fell on deaf ears. Teary-eyed, the gardener went to Birbal, who whispered a secret in his ear. Next day, Akbar asked the gardener about his last wish. The gardener cleared his throat and spat on Akbar's foot. He had acted on Birbal's advice. Everyone stared in disbelief. Then Birbal spoke. He said, "Your Majesty, this gardener is very loyal towards you. He was worried that people would dislike you for punishing him severely for a small mistake. So he committed a crime which was appropriate for a death sentence." Akbar realised his mistake and pardoned the gardener.

25. *Music to the Bull's Ears*

One day, Akbar told Birbal, "There shall be a huge music competition next week. Invite the best musicians and Birbal, you shall participate, too." On the day of the competition, when the participants had gathered in the royal hall, Akbar announced, "I'm sure you're all great musicians in your own right. But the winner will be decided by our guest." As everyone looked in surprise, a bull was brought in. Akbar said, "The one who impresses this bull shall win." The musicians were shocked but they had no choice. One by one, they played the best music on earth but the bull did not care. At last, it was Birbal's turn. He produced the sound of mooing cows and droning mosquitoes with his musical instrument. At once, the bull looked at Birbal and showed interest in the music. Akbar said, "Birbal is the winner, since he performed according to the audience's choice."

26. *Nothing is Permanent*

Akbar became king when he was just 13. Eventually, he formed a vast empire. He knew he was a great man and this made him arrogant. Due to this, Akbar acted inconsiderately towards his subjects at times. Birbal did not like this since Akbar was otherwise a kind man. One day, Birbal disguised himself as a saint and went to the royal garden. When Akbar came for a stroll, he saw the saint and said, "How dare you enter my garden? You shall be sentenced to death." The saint said, "Is this your garden?" Arrogantly, Akbar said, "Yes!" "Then," said the saint, "the rivers, the trees and the country all belong to you?" Akbar said, "Yes!" The saint asked, "Who owned them before they belonged to you?" Akbar realised that nothing was permanent. What was his today would belong to someone else tomorrow. This knowledge ended the arrogance within him.

27. *Birbal and the Ironsmith*

One day, Akbar and Birbal were lost in a discussion when the royal ironsmith entered the court. The ironsmith made swords and shields for Akbar's army. He announced, "Your Majesty, I have made the strongest sword and shield in the world. No sword can pierce the shield I have made." Then he held a sword and said, "This is the sharpest sword in the world. It is so sharp that it can cut through the strongest of shields." Birbal was listening to all this and said, "How can the sword and the shield be equally strong? If your shield can protect from the sharpest of swords, the sword you have crafted cannot be the sharpest in the world. And if your sword cuts through the shield you have made, it cannot be the strongest shield in the world." Akbar was impressed with Birbal's observation. He gifted the sword and the shield to Birbal.

28. *Six Kings of Persia*

The king of Persia had heard many stories of Birbal's wit and wisdom. He wanted to know whether Birbal was indeed intelligent and was eager to meet him. So he sent his messenger with a special invitation to visit Persia. Birbal accepted the invitation. When Birbal reached the king's court, he saw six kings sitting on six thrones. All the kings looked exactly the same. Birbal was amazed to see this. Then he understood that the king of Persia wanted to test him. Without much thought, Birbal bowed before the real king. The king was impressed. He asked Birbal, "Dear Birbal, how did you know I'm the king?" Birbal replied, "All the others were looking at you, as if awaiting further instructions, but only you looked straight ahead, just as a leader does. Only a king looks ahead with confidence, while his subjects look up to him for advice."

29. *The Copper Coin*

One day, Akbar called Birbal to his court and had a long discussion. When their conversation ended, Birbal bowed and turned to leave. Just then, a copper coin fell from his pocket. As Birbal bent to pick the coin up, a jealous courtier said, "Your Majesty, you have showered Birbal with wealth, yet he remains a miser. He is looking for a copper coin." Birbal noticed that Akbar was getting upset with the courtier's comment. He immediately said, "Your Majesty, one side of the coin has your face on it. I can't bear the thought of anyone stepping on it. That's why I'm so keen on picking it up." Akbar was impressed. He told the jealous courtier, "Birbal is not only clever, but also loyal towards me." Saying this, he took off his diamond ring and gifted it to Birbal. The jealous courtier was annoyed, but he couldn't do anything.

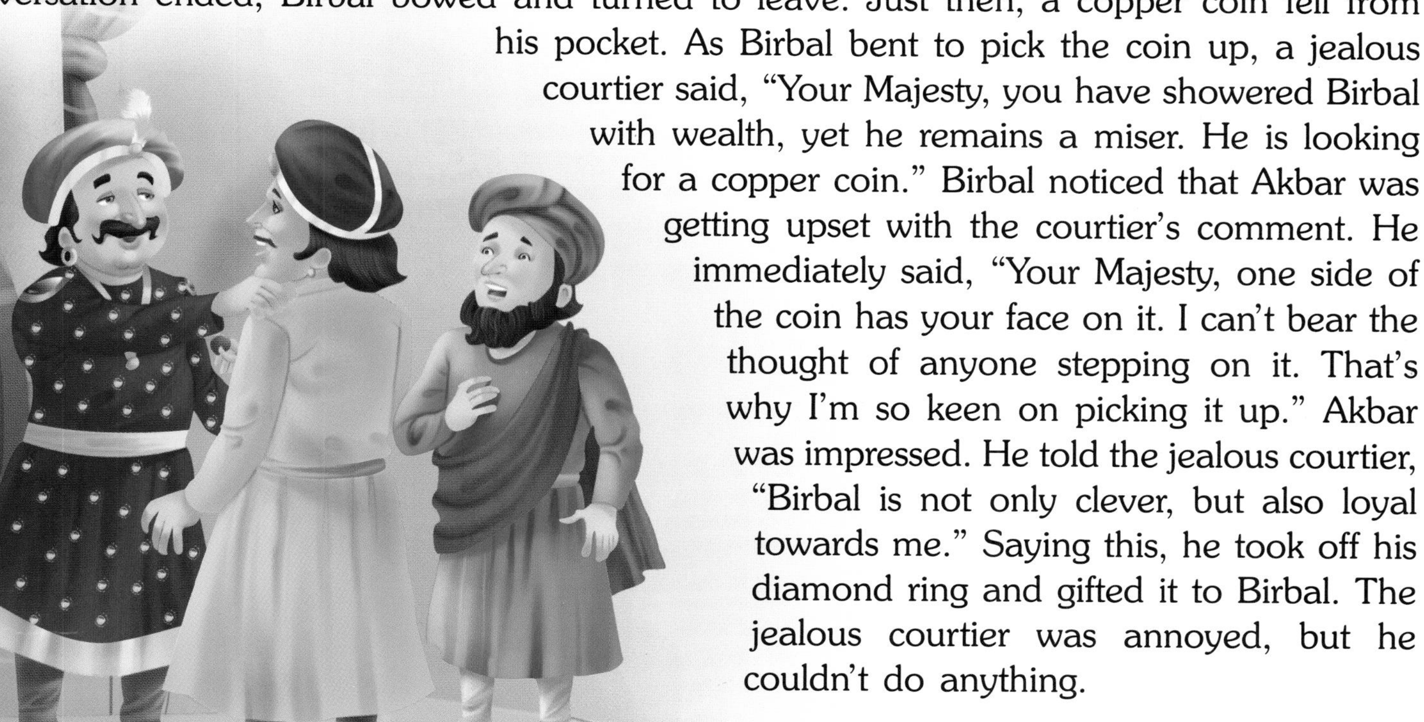

30. *Birbal Saves a Life*

Akbar was a benevolent king but he also had an awful temper. One day, he got angry with one of his courtiers. He was so furious that he ordered the guards to behead him the next day. The courtier fell at Birbal's feet and pleaded, "Birbal! Please save me from the Emperor's wrath." Birbal offered him advice. Next day, the courtier stood near the palace gates, where one of the guards saw him. The guard was taking him away when the courtier said, "I want to see the Emperor before I die." The guard reluctantly agreed. When Akbar saw the courtier, he asked the guard, "I had asked you to behead him. Why is he here?" The courtier knelt in front of Akbar and said, "Your Majesty, you wanted my head. So I decided to bring it to you." Akbar smiled and said, "Very well. You may keep it with you."

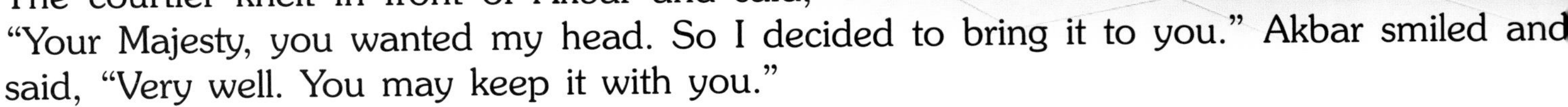

31. *Birbal and the Stable-Boy*

When Akbar saw Birbal, his favourite minister, walking to the court, he was annoyed. He asked, "Birbal, why are you walking? Where are your horses?" Birbal replied, "Your Majesty, my wife and her cousins have taken the horses. They have gone to visit relatives." Akbar summoned the stable-boy and ordered him to give Birbal a horse. The stable-boy chose the weakest horse. The horse was sick and reached Birbal's stable in great pain. At night, the horse died. Next day, Birbal walked to the court. When Akbar asked him about the horse, Birbal said, "Your Majesty, the horse you gave me was so fast that he reached heaven last night." Akbar scolded the stable-boy and said, "Why did you give Birbal a sick horse? You shall be whipped." Birbal said, "Please pardon him, Your Majesty." The stable-boy was ashamed. He thanked Birbal for saving him and chose a handsome horse for Birbal.

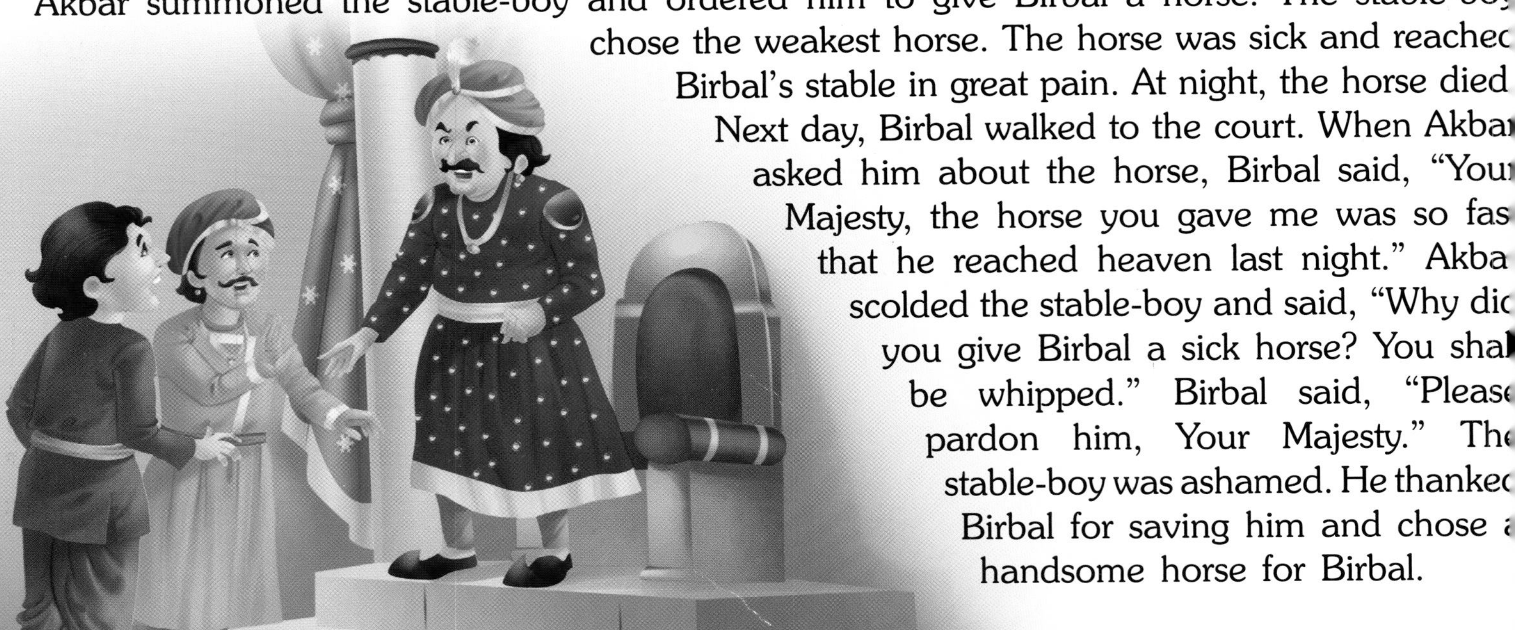

32. *Birbal and the Magical Donkey*

One of Akbar's courtiers rushed to him and said, "There was a theft in my house last night. All my valuables are gone." Akbar said, "How can that be? You live in a safe locality." Then Akbar called Birbal and said, "One of the courtiers must be the culprit." Birbal said, "I will find out, Your Majesty," and he left the court. Soon, he returned with a donkey and said, "This magical donkey will tell us who the thief is." Then he asked all the courtiers to lift the donkey's tail and say, "I am not the thief." One by one, the courtiers followed Birbal's instructions. In the end, Birbal asked them to raise their hands. Everyone's hands were black. But there was one courtier whose hands were clean. Birbal pointed towards him and said, "Here is our thief. He was scared of the magical donkey. So he did not touch the tail."

33. *Truth and Falsehood*

Akbar occasionally put his courtiers' intelligence to test and asked them all kinds of difficult questions. One day, he asked them, "What is the difference between truth and falsehood? Tell me your answer in less than three words." All the courtiers were taken aback. They did not have the answer to his question and they were silent. Akbar asked, "Why is everyone quiet? Birbal, can you answer this?" Birbal said, "Your Majesty, I want everyone else to speak first. That's why I'm silent." Akbar said, "No one seems to know the answer. Go ahead; tell me in less than three words!" "Four fingers," said Birbal. Akbar was confused. Birbal explained, "Your Majesty, what we see is true but what we hear is mostly untrue. And the width between our eyes and ears is that of four fingers. That is what I meant." Akbar was pleased with Birbal's answer.

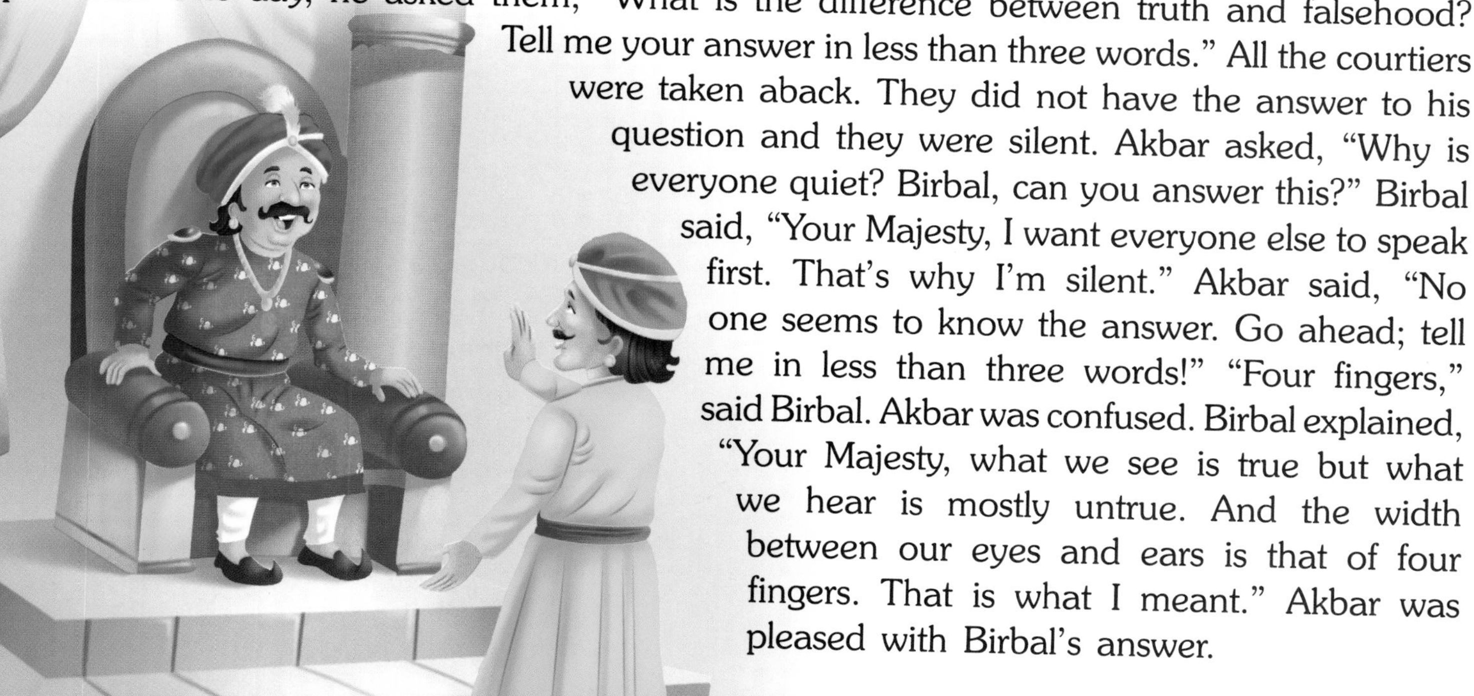

34. *Akbar Asks, Birbal Answers*

One day, Akbar announced, "I have five questions for everyone today. Let's see who is the most sensible among all of you." He asked, "Name the best flower." All the courtiers named different flowers. Birbal said, "The cotton flower, since cloth can be produced from it." Akbar asked, "Which is the best leaf?" The courtiers named the neem leaf. Birbal said, "The betel leaf, which is offered to friends and foes." Akbar asked, "Which is the best milk?" Everyone said, "Cow's milk!" But Birbal said, "Mother's milk, since it helps a baby grow. Akbar asked, "Where is sweetness?" While the courtiers named various sweets, Birbal said, "In the tongue, since it is capable of tasting." Akbar asked, "Who is the best king?" All the courtiers said, "You!" But Birbal said, "King Indra, because he sends rain, which helps crops grow, and we get our food." Akbar liked all of Birbal's answers.

35. *One-eyed Abdul Karim*

One of Akbar's courtiers went by the name Abdul Karim. He was blind in one eye. He was also jealous of Birbal. He spared no chance to spoil Akbar's impression of Birbal. One day, Karim saw Birbal spitting betel nuts on a palace wall. He went to Akbar and complained about Birbal. Akbar was annoyed. He said, "Birbal, why did you spit on the palace wall? Next time, spit in an empty, useless place." Birbal apologised to Akbar. Next day, after chewing betel nuts, Birbal spat into Karim's blind eye. Karim went running to Akbar. Akbar roared, "Birbal! What is this?" Birbal bowed and said, "Your Majesty! Karim's blind eye is empty and useless, so I spat in it!" Akbar laughed. He told Karim, "It's not right to tell tales. When you saw Birbal spitting on the wall, you should have asked him not to do so instead of complaining to me."

36. *Hairless Palms*

One day, when Birbal entered the court, he saw Akbar sitting quietly on his throne, staring at his hands. Birbal bowed and asked, "Is all well, Your Majesty?" Akbar asked Birbal, "Why are my palms hairless?" After thinking for a while, Birbal said, "You are very generous, Your Majesty! You always shower everyone around you with gifts and money. You always give away things to the poor and the needy as well. Your palms are always rubbing against the gifts. Hence, no hair can grow on them." Akbar's eyes twinkled in amusement. He asked, "Birbal, why doesn't hair grow on your palms?" Birbal replied, "Your Majesty, you always give me rewards and gifts. My palms rub against them every now and then. So my palms are hairless as well." Akbar smiled at Birbal's quick-wittedness. He said, "Here's one more gift for your quick reply. Take my diamond necklace," and he handed it to Birbal.

37. *Birbal, the Magician*

One day, a jealous courtier tried to plot against Birbal. Before Birbal entered the royal court, the courtier had whispered in Akbar's ear, "Your Majesty, Birbal is neglecting his duty and indulging in useless pursuits. I've heard that he is learning magic." When Birbal came to the court, Akbar asked, "Birbal, I heard you know magic. I have lost my ring. Can you find it?" Birbal understood that this was the work of a jealous courtier. He said, "Yes, Your Majesty! I will chant a spell, and the ring will be on your finger." Saying this, Birbal began to chant some mysterious words. Akbar had actually given his ring to the jealous courtier and asked him to hide it in his pocket. The courtier was scared that the ring would fly away, so he held it tight. Birbal noticed this and said, "The ring is with him!" Akbar smiled.

38. *The Wine Jugs*

Birbal noticed that Akbar had been absent from the court for long stretches of time. This worried him a lot. So he went to the palace to enquire about his well-being. Just as he entered the palace, he overheard Akbar saying silly things to himself. Then he entered Akbar's bedroom and looked around. He found many jugs of wine. He picked a wine jug up and turned to leave. Just then, Akbar saw him. Birbal hid the jug in his shawl. Akbar asked, "What are you hiding?" Birbal said, "It's a parrot. No, it's a horse. It's an elephant. No, it's a donkey!" Akbar was puzzled. Birbal explained, "Your Majesty, wine makes one talk like a parrot and act like a horse. It makes one walk like an elephant. It turns a man into a donkey. Please don't drink." Akbar realised his folly and threw away all the jugs of wine.

39. *Judgement and Justice*

Akbar always sought Birbal's advice on important matters. One day, after solving a difficult case and passing a judgement, Akbar asked Birbal, "Tell me when God shows His justice." Birbal thought for a while. Then he said, "Your Majesty, when your judgement is not right, we can see God's justice." Akbar said, "I did not understand what you just said. Could you please explain, Birbal?" Birbal answered, "Your Majesty, as our Emperor, you are the representative of God on earth. But when you, somehow, pass a wrong judgement, God not only sees it, but also sets it right. That's when we get to see God's justice." Akbar was impressed with Birbal's answer. He always kept this answer in mind whenever he was about to pass a judgement. Thus, he avoided injustice. He came to be known among his subjects as a kind and just ruler, who was loved by all.

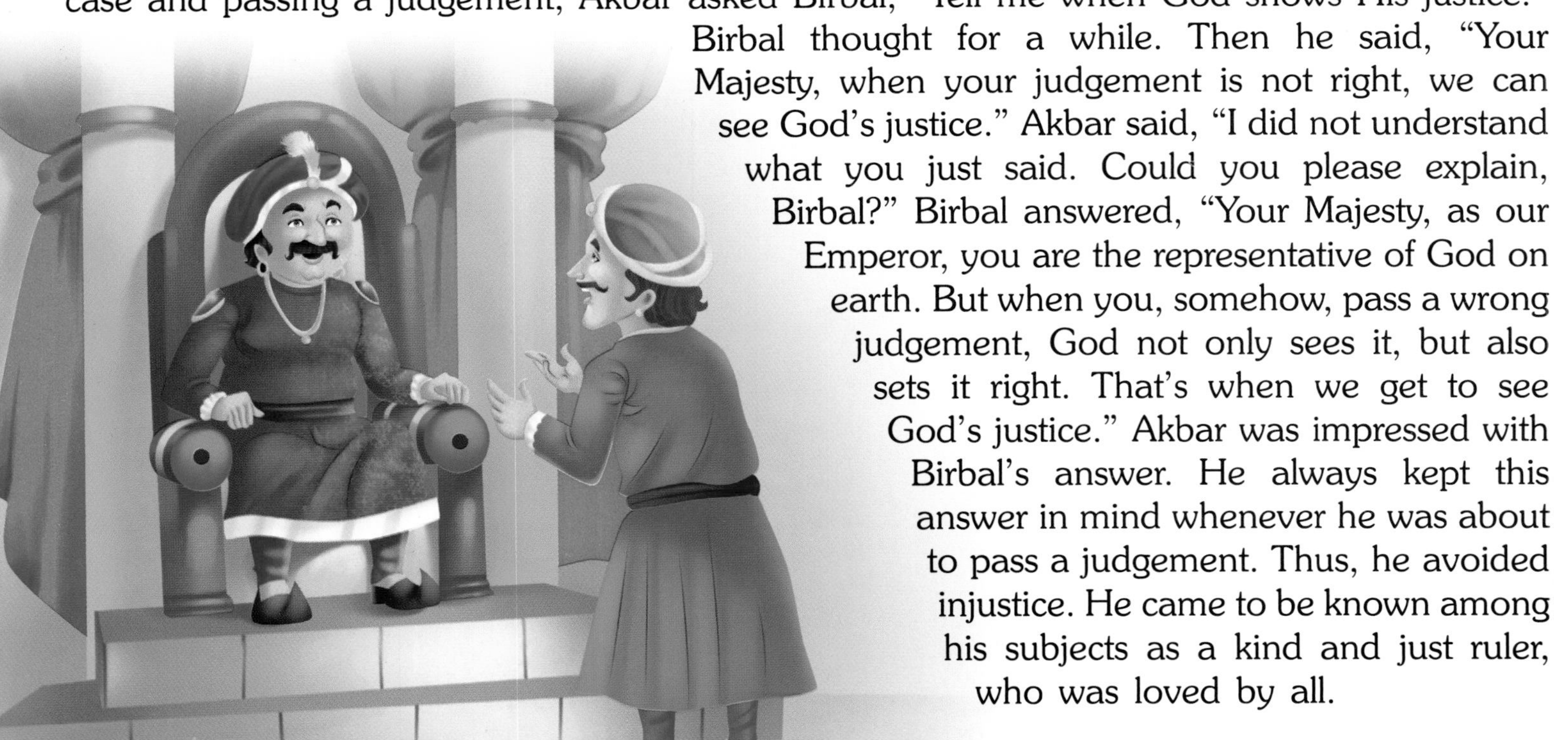

40. *The Learned and the Foolish*

One day, Akbar decided to ask Birbal a difficult question. He asked, "Birbal, what is the difference between a foolish man and a learned man?" Birbal smiled and replied, "Your Majesty! A learned man always uses his brains when he is in a difficult situation. He is always calm and does not lose control." Akbar asked, "And what does a foolish man do?" Birbal replied, "Your Majesty, a foolish man has no control over difficult situations. He doesn't use his brains and handles the situation badly. He either spoils the task at hand or makes the situation worse." Once again, Akbar was impressed with Birbal's answer. Akbar had thought that Birbal would answer like the other courtiers and say that an uneducated person was foolish, while the one who was educated was learned. Birbal's answer helped to cement the special relationship that he shared with the Emperor.

41. *Akbar, the Jovial Emperor*

Akbar was not only a generous, just ruler, but he was also very cheerful and jovial. He loved to play pranks and have fun occasionally. One day, he was in the mood for a joke. He was waiting for Birbal, since he knew Birbal's witty answers would add to the fun. When Birbal entered the court, he asked, "Tell me, Birbal; what is the difference between you and a donkey?" Birbal looked at Akbar, who was seated on the throne, and then he turned his eyes towards the floor, where he stood. He appeared to be deep in thought. Akbar said, "It seems you are calculating something. Am I right?" Birbal bowed and said, "Yes, Your Majesty. Now that I have made the calculation, here is my answer: The difference between me and a donkey is eight feet in distance!" Akbar loved the joke. He laughed heartily at Birbal's wittiness.

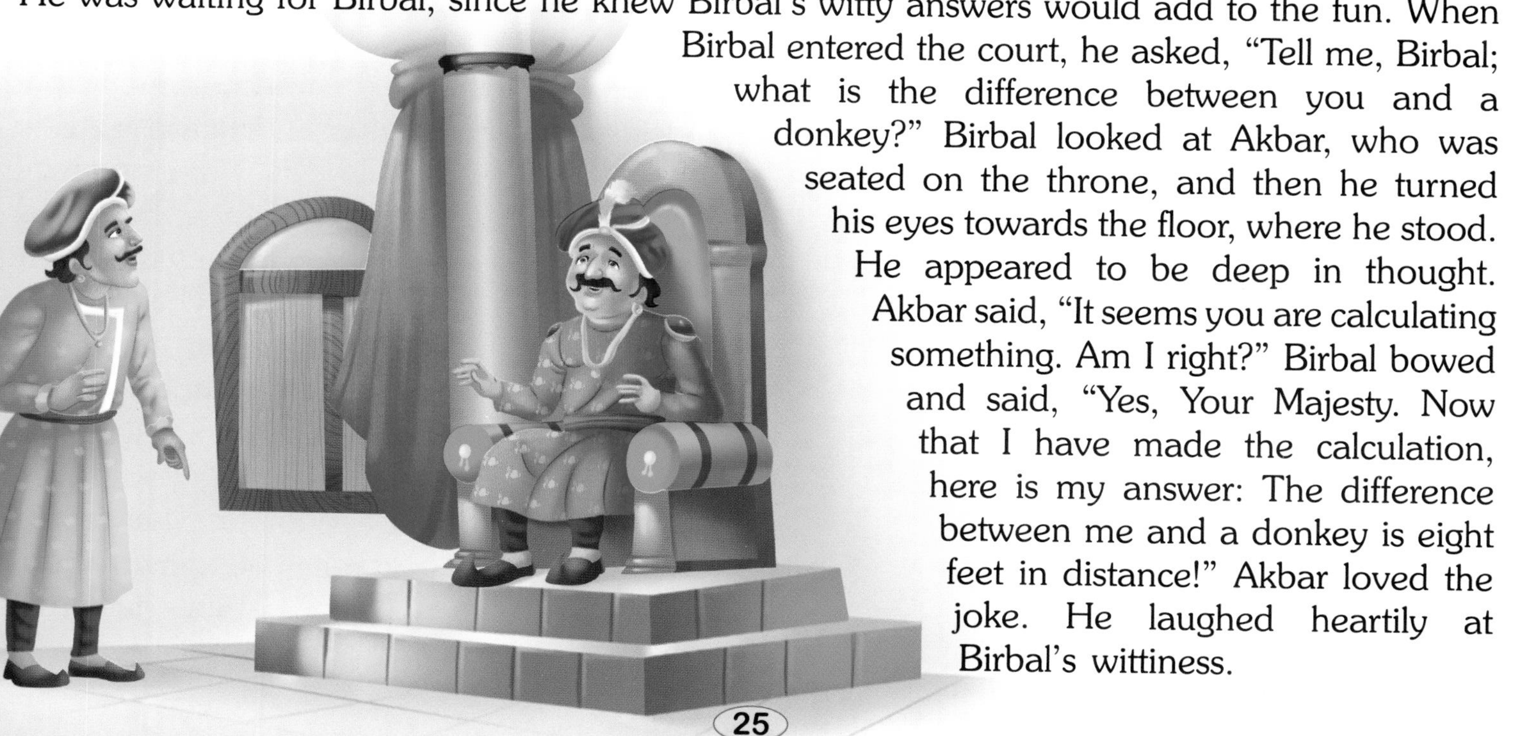

42. *The Shepherd Boy*

There were many reasons why Akbar was fond of Birbal. He offered valuable advice, cheered him up and fulfilled all his wishes, no matter how unusual they were. One day, Akbar asked Birbal to bring the most learned person to his court. Birbal agreed. But he had two conditions. He wanted a week's holiday and five hundred gold coins. Akbar agreed. Birbal distributed the gold coins among the needy people. Then, he spent his time teaching a shepherd boy how to behave in the royal court. After a week, Birbal presented the boy in Akbar's court. He told Akbar, "Here is the most learned person, Your Majesty." Akbar asked the boy, "What is special about you? Where do you live?" The boy was quiet. Akbar asked, "Why is he silent?" Birbal said, "His elders have taught him not to speak in front of anyone who is wiser than he." Akbar was pleased.

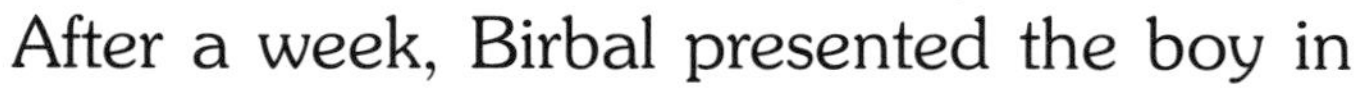

43. *The Mad Elephant*

One day, Akbar's courtiers were discussing the best weapon. All the courtiers named different weapons. But Birbal said, "There is no such weapon. Whatever comes handy at the time of danger is the best weapon." Akbar did not agree. Next day, when Akbar and Birbal were walking through the city, a mad elephant chased them. Akbar tried to attack it with his sword, but in vain. As they ran for their lives, Birbal saw a puppy playing by the roadside. He picked it up and threw it at the elephant. The puppy clung to the elephant's trunk. Its claws pierced the elephant and it stopped chasing them. Akbar heaved a sigh of relief. Birbal said, "Your Majesty, the puppy was our best weapon in this situation." Akbar praised Birbal. He said, "Birbal, you saved my life today and taught me a great lesson about weapons." Then he gave Birbal a pearl necklace.

44. *Ruling Forever*

One evening, Akbar and Birbal were enjoying a stroll in the garden Akbar said, "Birbal! Wouldn't it be wonderful if a person who becomes an emperor is allowed to reign forever?" Birbal said, "Yes, Your Majesty! That sounds great. But there is a problem." Akbar asked, "What is it?" Birbal said, "If such a rule was to be followed, you would never have been our emperor." Akbar was taken aback. "Why do you say that, Birbal?" he asked. Birbal replied, "Your Majesty, if your grandfather who was previously the emperor, ruled forever, your father could not have succeeded to the throne. In turn, you would also have lost the chance to become the emperor. How can you forget that Your Majesty is the grandson of your grandfather?" Akbar praised Birbal's logic and common sense. He said, "The thought never crossed my mind, Birbal. You are so wise!"

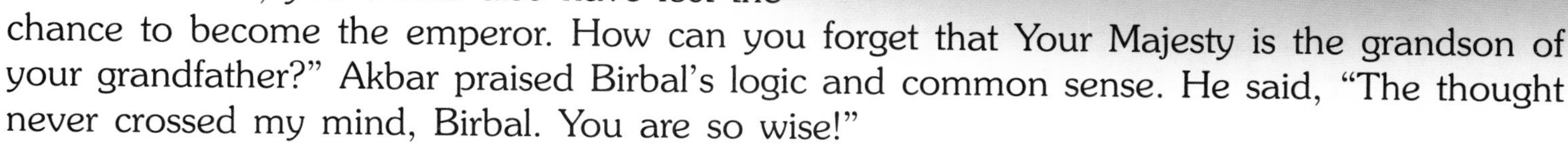

45. *Birbal Has the Answer*

Akbar was very intelligent. He liked to sharpen his knowledge and test his courtiers' intelligence as well. One day, he asked them, "What is that one thing in the world which is ever moving?" The courtiers began discussing among themselves and came up with many answers. Some said it is the sun. Some said it is the moon. Yet, others said it is the earth that moves forever. But Akbar did not agree to any of their answers. Then he turned to Birbal and asked him the question. Birbal said, "Your Majesty, the interest on the money which is borrowed is ever moving since it keeps growing without fail and never gets tired. The interest keeps moving until the borrowed amount is fully paid back to the moneylender." Akbar was satisfied with Birbal's answer. He said, "Birbal, I knew that no one would be able to answer this question except you."

46. *The Horse Trader*

Once, a horse trader came to visit Akbar. He had some fine horses and wanted the emperor to buy them. Akbar liked the horses and bought a few of them. He wanted more horses and paid money in advance to the trader. The trader said, "I shall bring the horses tomorrow, Your Majesty," and left. He never returned. Birbal did not like the way his emperor had been cheated. One day, when Akbar asked Birbal to make a list of fools in the kingdom, Birbal included Akbar's name in it. Akbar was furious and demanded to know why Birbal had called him a fool. Birbal replied, "Didn't a horse trader cheat you once?" Akbar said, "So what?" Birbal replied, "Why did you trust a stranger without inquiring about him first? I will remove your name from this list of fools when the horse trader returns." Akbar realised his mistake.

47. *The Farmer's Well*

Akbar was in the royal court, listening to the complaints of the people of his kingdom. Birbal was also near him. Just then, a farmer and his neighbour entered the court. The farmer said, "Your Majesty, I am a poor farmer. My neighbour sold me his well a few months ago. But now he also wants me to pay for the water." The neighbour said, "Yes, Your Majesty! I need money for the water in the well." Akbar thought, 'This sounds interesting. Birbal should solve it.' Birbal heard the farmer's story and told the neighbour, "You sold only your well to the farmer. So the well belongs to him. But the water belongs to you. Since you have kept your water in the farmer's well, you either pay him rent or remove the water." The neighbour realised that he had been selfish. The farmer thanked Birbal for helping him out.

48. *Bright, White Sunlight*

One day, Akbar asked, "What is the whitest and brightest of all?" All the courtiers began discussing what it could be. Some of them felt cotton is the brightest and whitest, while others said it is milk. When Akbar asked Birbal, he replied, "Sunlight, Your Majesty." Akbar asked Birbal to prove it. When Akbar went for a nap, he asked that the curtains of his bedroom be drawn. When he woke up and walked towards the door, he tripped over something on the floor. He opened the door and sunlight streamed in. He saw a bowl of milk on the floor, and some cotton strewn beside it. "Who kept these things here?" Akbar shouted. Birbal said, "I did, Your Majesty. If milk and cotton were the whitest, you could have seen these in the dark. But you could see them only in the sunlight. So, isn't sunlight the whitest and brightest?" Akbar praised Birbal's common sense.

49. *Birbal in Exile*

One day, when the court was in session, Akbar's favourite queen sent word that she wanted to see him. Akbar wanted to finish his work before he left. Soon, the queen sent another messenger asking for the emperor. As Akbar got up to leave, he saw Birbal smiling in a silly manner. Furious, he said, "Birbal! Go away and don't ever set foot on my soil." Birbal got up and left quietly. Those who were jealous of Birbal were happy. A month passed thus. Akbar missed Birbal's sensible advice. One day, when Akbar looked out of his window, he saw Birbal riding a chariot. He called Birbal and asked, "Why are you disobeying me?" Birbal said, "Your Majesty, you asked me not to step on your soil. So I sprinkled soil from the neighbouring kingdom on this chariot. I will step on it throughout my life." Akbar laughed heartily and forgave Birbal.

50. *The Brinjal Dish*

One day, during lunch, Akbar and Birbal were served a dish made of brinjal. Akbar liked it very much. He said, "Birbal, there is nothing tastier than this dish, is there?" Birbal said, "You are right, Your Majesty." Akbar called his chef and said, "This dish is very tasty. Please give Birbal some more brinjal." Birbal said, "This dish is tasty but I will not have more, Your Majesty. I don't like brinjal." Akbar was confused. He said, "How can that be? You just said that the dish is tasty. How can you dislike brinjal?" "Your Majesty, I am your servant. It is my duty to agree with you. But I cannot change my taste. I really dislike brinjal," said Birbal. Akbar said, "This is a surprising revelation, Birbal. But I accept it. I am glad you are honest with me and did not try to flatter me."

51. *Donkey in the Tobacco Field*

One day, Akbar and Birbal went for a long walk. They passed by many lush fields. As they continued to walk, enjoying the beautiful weather, they passed a tobacco field. Just then, a hungry donkey walked into the tobacco field. But when the donkey went near the tobacco plants, it turned away in disgust. Since Birbal used to chew tobacco sometimes, Akbar said, "Did you see, Birbal? Even donkeys don't chew tobacco."

Birbal quipped, "Your Majesty, donkeys don't chew tobacco because they don't have the sense to appreciate it." Akbar said, "Birbal, I like your witty response, but you know that tobacco is bad for your health, don't you? Chewing tobacco is a very harmful habit and you must stop." Birbal knew that Akbar wished him well and that he was speaking the truth. He said, "Your Majesty, I know that you are right. I will stop chewing tobacco."

52. *Season of Mangoes*

It was the season of mangoes. Akbar's subjects gifted him with many boxes of the fruit. After Akbar and Birbal had lunch together, they sunk their teeth into the juicy mangoes and relished their taste. They were having a good time, chatting and eating mangoes. When they would finish eating mangoes, they would throw the seeds under the table. After Akbar had his fill, he was in the mood to play a prank. He pushed all the mango seeds from his side to Birbal's side. Then he said, "Birbal! I know you like mangoes, but I didn't know you were so greedy. Look at how many mangoes you have eaten!" Birbal looked under the table and saw that all the mango seeds were on his side. Cleverly, he replied, "Your Majesty, I like mangoes, but not so much as you. You have eaten the seeds too!" Akbar smiled in response.

53. *Manohar and Misfortune*

One day, one of Akbar's courtiers told him about a man named Manohar. He said, "Your Majesty, whoever sees Manohar's face gets into trouble." Akbar said, "I don't believe you. I want to see Manohar tomorrow." Next day, Manohar entered the court. Akbar had barely seen him when he received news that one of his granaries was on fire. As Akbar left his throne and hurried down the stairs, he fell. That's when he remembered that Manohar was unlucky. He said, "Manohar, it is your fault. Guards! Arrest him!" On the way to the jail, Manohar told Birbal about the incident. Birbal whispered a secret in Manohar's ear. Next day, Akbar visited Manohar in jail. Manohar said, "Your Majesty, you say I am unlucky. But I saw your face and now I am in jail! Who is more unlucky?" Akbar realised that misfortune had nothing to do with Manohar and set him free.

54. *The Servant's Plight*

One morning, Akbar looked into the mirror. Suddenly, he called his servant and said, "Go and call him now." The obedient servant rushed out but soon realised that he didn't know who he was supposed to call. But he was terrified of asking Akbar lest the emperor should be furious. So he went to Birbal instead and narrated his plight. Birbal asked the servant, "What was the emperor doing when he called you?" The servant said, "He was looking into the mirror." Birbal said, "It means the emperor noticed that his hair had grown long. He wanted to see the barber." After the servant had left, Akbar realised that he had not told the servant whom to call. Soon, the servant entered his room with the barber. Akbar was surprised. He asked, "How did you know I wanted to see the barber?" The servant replied, "Birbal told me, Your Majesty." Akbar admired Birbal's wisdom.

55. *The Half-Brother*

When Akbar was young, his nurse took care of him like her son. She would feed him her milk when his mother was away. Akbar respected her a lot and treated her like his mother. He considered the nurse's son as his half-brother. Akbar loved his half-brother and made lavish arrangements whenever his half-brother came to see him. Sometimes, Akbar stayed absent from the court to spend time with his half-brother. Birbal did not want Akbar to neglect his duties. So, when Akbar asked Birbal, "Do you also have a half-brother?" Birbal replied, "Yes, I shall bring him tomorrow, Your Majesty." Next day, Birbal brought a calf to the court. Akbar shouted, "Birbal! What is this animal doing here?" Birbal replied, "Your Majesty, this is my half-brother. Since childhood, I've been feeding on the milk of his mother, the cow." Akbar understood Birbal's message and stopped giving undue importance to his half-brother.

56. *The Courtiers and the Shawl*

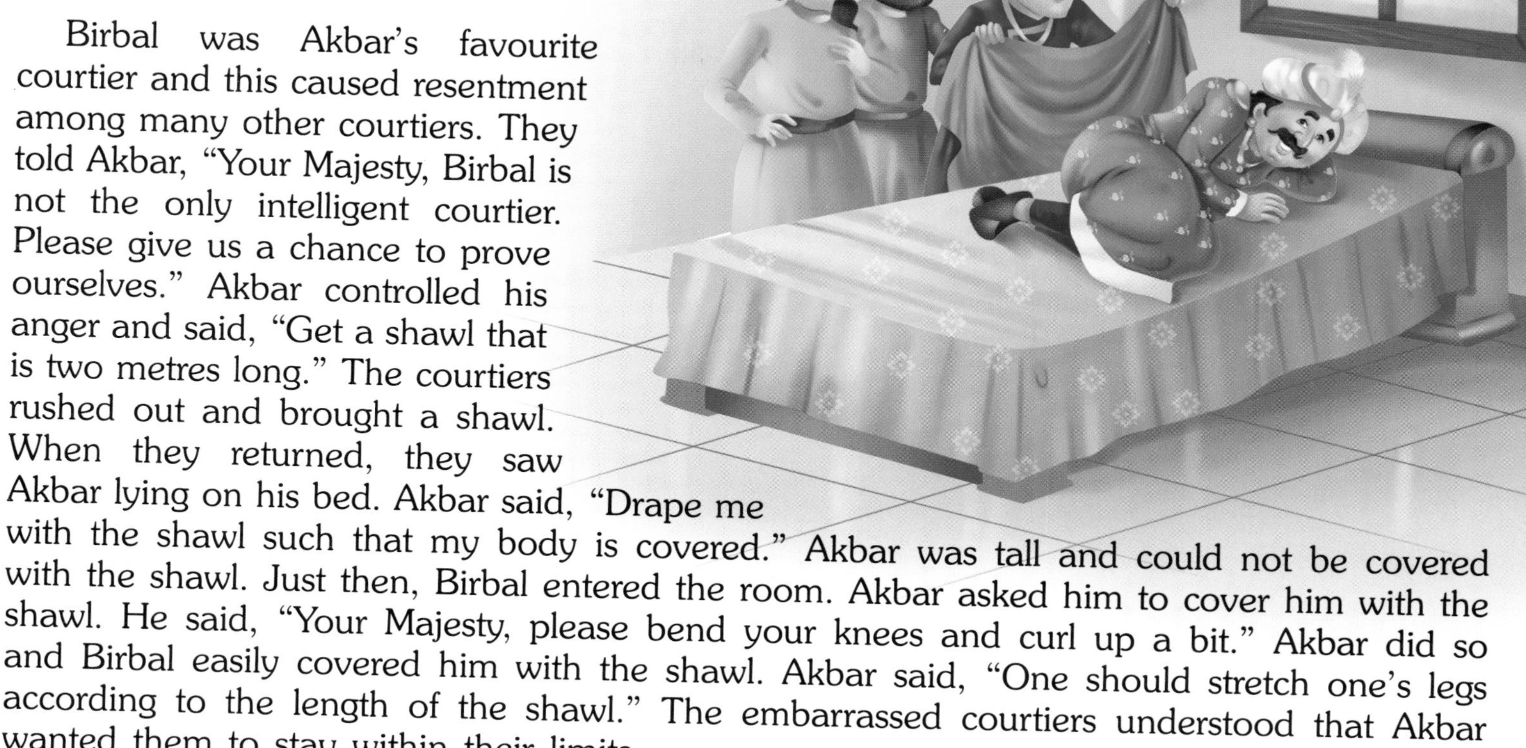

Birbal was Akbar's favourite courtier and this caused resentment among many other courtiers. They told Akbar, "Your Majesty, Birbal is not the only intelligent courtier. Please give us a chance to prove ourselves." Akbar controlled his anger and said, "Get a shawl that is two metres long." The courtiers rushed out and brought a shawl. When they returned, they saw Akbar lying on his bed. Akbar said, "Drape me with the shawl such that my body is covered." Akbar was tall and could not be covered with the shawl. Just then, Birbal entered the room. Akbar asked him to cover him with the shawl. He said, "Your Majesty, please bend your knees and curl up a bit." Akbar did so and Birbal easily covered him with the shawl. Akbar said, "One should stretch one's legs according to the length of the shawl." The embarrassed courtiers understood that Akbar wanted them to stay within their limits.

57. *Birbal Catches a Thief*

One day, a woman came to Akbar's court with a man. She said, "Your Majesty, this man snatched all my ornaments." The man said, "I'm a visitor, Your Majesty. This woman brought me here to meet you." Birbal asked the woman, "How much were your ornaments worth?" She said, "Six thousand gold coins." Birbal knew she could not afford so much gold. But he gave her the money. After she had left, Birbal whispered a secret to the man and a servant. They followed the woman. After a while, the man tried to snatch the woman's bag, but she held him by the collar and reached Akbar's court to complain against him. But the servant told Birbal what he had seen. Birbal asked the woman, "If this man could not snatch a bag from you, how could he have snatched ornaments from you?" The woman fell at Akbar's feet and begged for forgiveness.

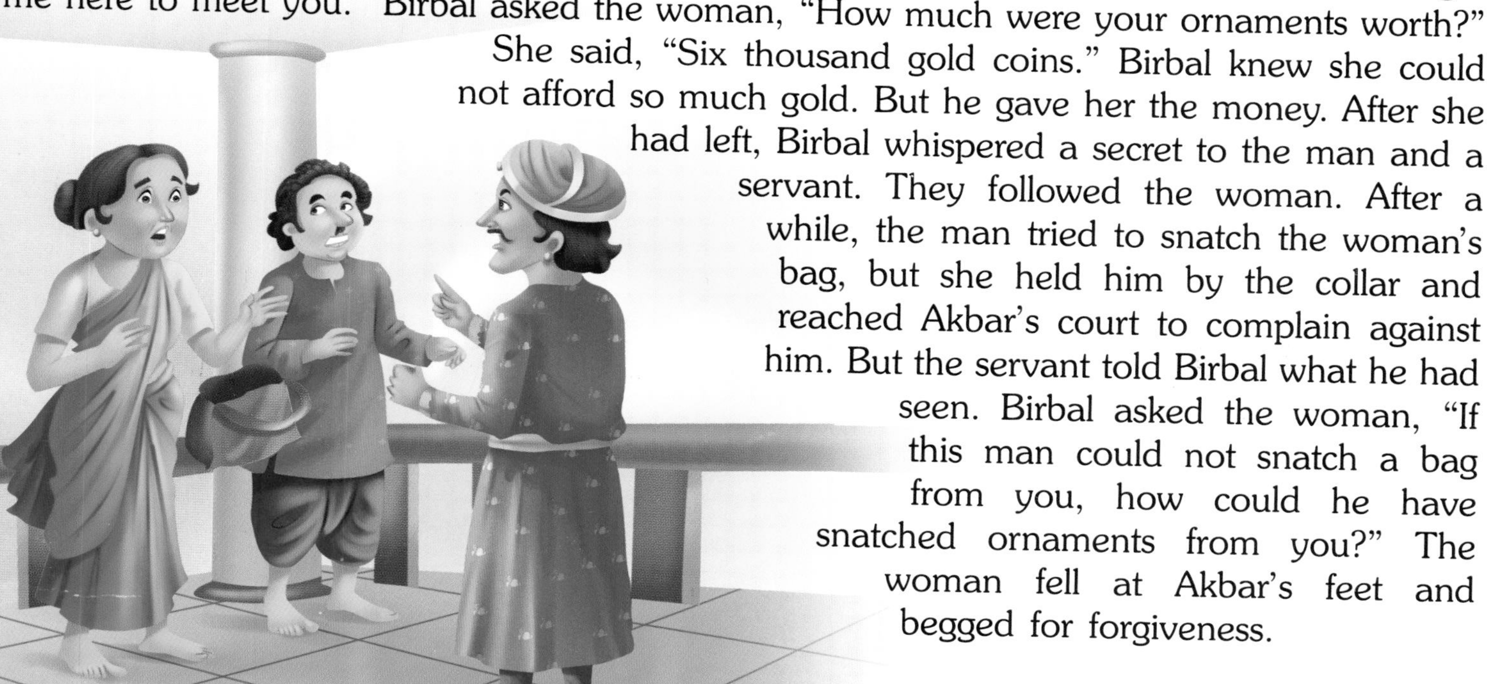

58. *A Tale of Opposites*

One day, Akbar said, "Birbal, I have a challenge for you." Birbal asked, "What is it, Your Majesty?" Akbar said, "Bring two persons to the court tomorrow. The first person should be extremely grateful and loyal." Birbal said, "How should the second person be?" Akbar smiled and said, "The second person should be the exact opposite. He should be an extremely ungrateful person who takes all favours for granted and keeps complaining, for he can never be satisfied." All the courtiers thought of this as an extremely difficult challenge and thought Birbal would lose. Next day, Birbal came to the court with his dog and his son-in-law. He pointed towards his dog and said, "My dog is grateful and faithful." Akbar said, "Who is this man?" Birbal said, "He is my son-in-law. He is always ungrateful and keeps complaining." Akbar clapped his hands and gave Birbal many gifts.

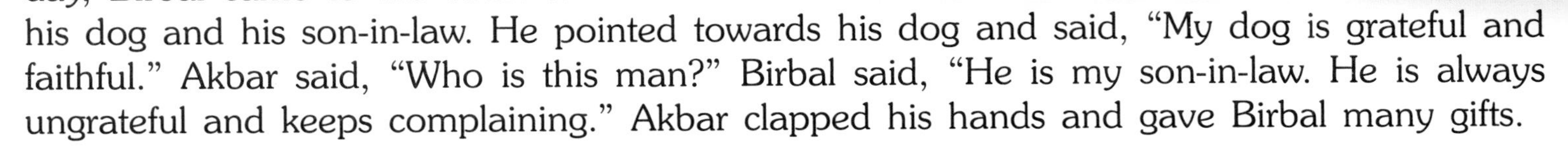

59. *Phases of the Moon*

Birbal's wisdom was famous all over the world. Once, a king from another kingdom wanted to meet Birbal. He invited Birbal to his palace. Birbal visited the king. The king was very impressed with Birbal's wit and wisdom. When Birbal's stay came to an end, the king gave him many gifts. As he left the palace, one of the king's ministers asked Birbal, "How would you compare Emperor Akbar with our king?" Birbal said, "Your king is like the full moon, while Emperor Akbar is like the crescent-shaped quarter moon." Everyone was happy with Birbal's answer. When Birbal reached Akbar's court, he came to know that his answer had angered Akbar. Akbar said, "You are not loyal to me. You have insulted me." Birbal explained, "Your Majesty! The full moon becomes smaller every day, while the quarter moon grows bigger. Your fame and power too is growing every day." Akbar hugged Birbal for his loyalty.

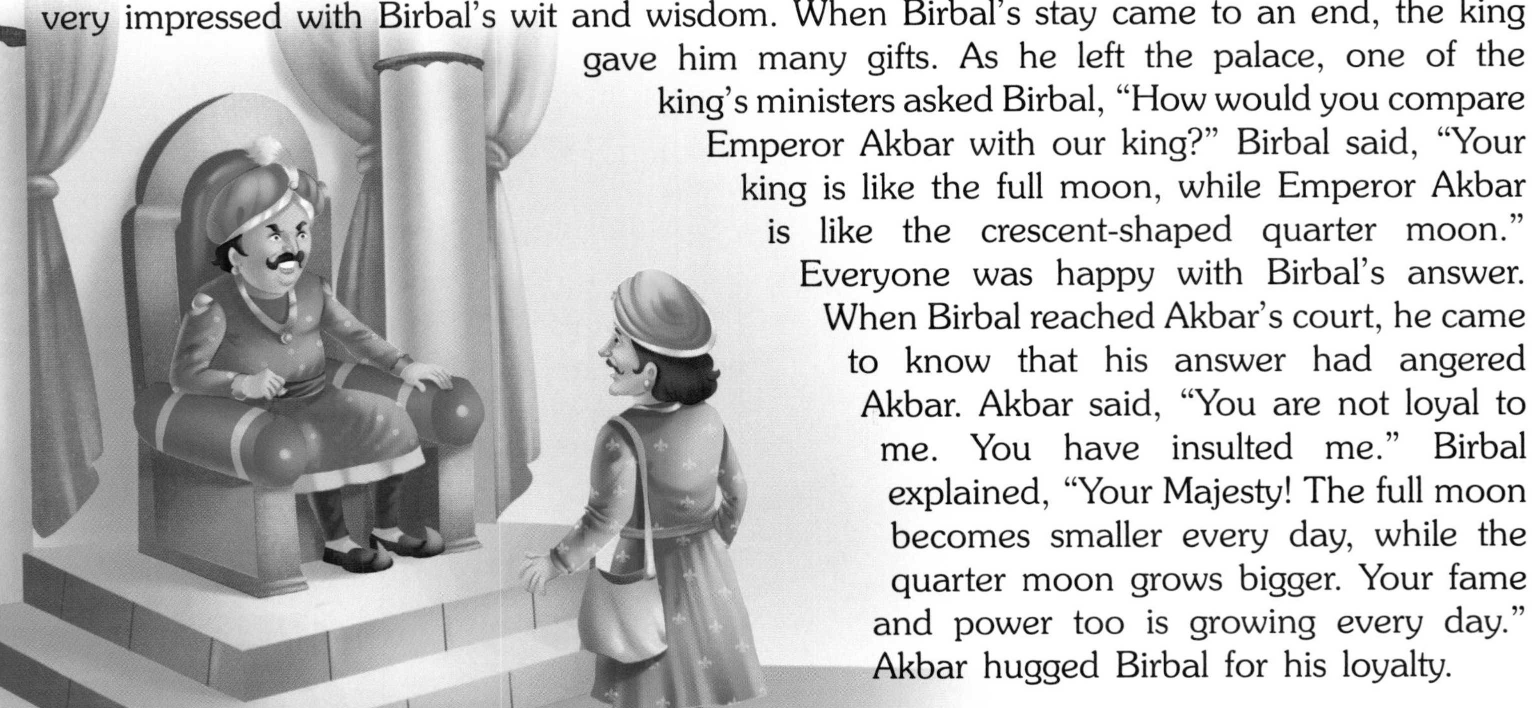

60. *Emperor for a Day*

One evening, Akbar, Birbal and several courtiers went for a boat ride. Akbar saw a twig floating by. He picked it up and said, "If any of you crosses this river just by holding this twig, I will make him emperor for a day." The courtiers felt this was impossible. But Birbal said, "I will do it if you declare me the emperor right now. The courtiers and the soldiers will be mine for today." Akbar agreed. Birbal took the twig and was about to jump into the river when a courtier shouted, "Stop, Your Majesty!" Birbal tried to jump again, but the soldiers stopped him. Whenever Birbal tried to jump, someone would stop him. After some time, they reached the shore. Akbar said, "You lost, Birbal!" Birbal said, "The courtiers and the soldiers did not let me jump. But I still held the twig while crossing the river. So I won!" Akbar smiled in affirmation.

61. *The Holy Parrot*

One day, Akbar's servant, Sevakram, rushed to visit Birbal. He looked scared. Birbal asked, "What is the matter, Sevakram?" Sevakram said, "A holy man had gifted a parrot to the emperor. His Majesty had asked me to take care of the bird. But he had also said whoever would inform him about its death would be hanged." Birbal asked, "So? Is the parrot dead?" "Yes," Sevakram frowned. "And I don't know how to tell His Majesty." Birbal said, "Don't worry. Let me handle this." Sevakram thanked Birbal and left. Birbal went to Akbar and said, "Your Majesty, your parrot is a holy bird. It is deep in meditation." Akbar was surprised. When he saw the parrot, he said, "Can't you see it's dead?" Birbal replied, "Your Majesty, everything that is born must die. Why should Sevakram be punished for this?" Akbar realised the truth and thanked Birbal.

62. *The Peeling Plaster*

One day, Akbar noticed that the plaster had peeled off in some of the rooms. “Dholak! I want these walls repaired immediately,” he ordered his servant. The next day, Akbar saw that the walls had not been repaired. He was angry. “Dholak! Come here!” he screamed. Dholak looked at the walls and said, “Pardon me, Your Majesty! I did not have the time to repair them.” “Bring a bowl of lime!” Akbar roared. Dholak went to get the bowl of lime and he saw Birbal there. Birbal asked Dholak to take some butter along with the lime. When Akbar asked Dholak to eat the lime, Dholak ate the butter. Akbar was surprised when Dholak did not get sick. He went to see what he was eating. He saw the butter and asked, “Did Birbal ask you to do this?” Dholak said frightfully, “Yes, Your Majesty.” Akbar laughed heartily and pardoned him.

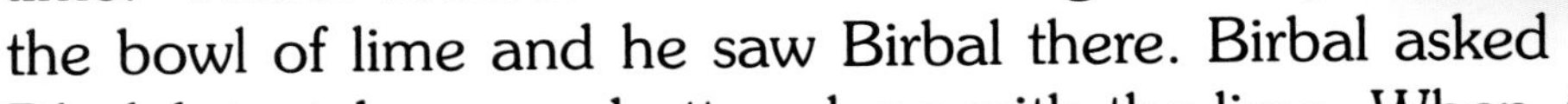

63. *The Portrait*

One day, Fazalji, the royal painter, went to Birbal. He said, “Please help me.” Birbal asked, “What happened?” Fazalji replied, “Liaqat Ali asked me for a portrait. I spent a day painting his picture. He had a beard and a moustache then. But the next day, Liaqat Ali refused to accept it. He had shaved off his beard and said the painting did not look exactly like him. I had to paint another portrait of him without the beard. But now he has shaved his moustache and refuses to accept it.” Birbal whispered his plan in Fazalji’s ear. Fazalji met Liaqat Ali and gave him a package and said, “Your portrait is ready.” Liaqat Ali opened the package and found a mirror. “Where is my painting?” he fumed. “Only a mirror can fulfil your ever-changing demands,” he said. Liaqat Ali realised his mistake. He paid Fazalji’s for all the portraits.

64. *A Pot of Intelligence*

One day, a messenger from a distant kingdom visited Akbar's court. He said, "O Emperor, our king has heard many tales of your courtiers and their intelligence. He wants a pot of intelligence from your kingdom." Akbar whispered to Birbal, "This king is making fun of us. How can we fill a pot with intelligence?" Birbal said reassuringly, "I can arrange for that but it will take a few weeks." The messenger was willing to wait. Birbal bought a few small-mouthed earthen pots. He planted pumpkin seeds in them. After a few weeks, there were little pumpkins in the pots. Next day, Birbal gave the messenger a pot and said, "The fruit of intelligence will be effective only if it is removed without damaging the pot." But the messenger couldn't empty the pot without breaking it. He left the court without uttering a word. Akbar said, "Birbal! You have saved my honour!"

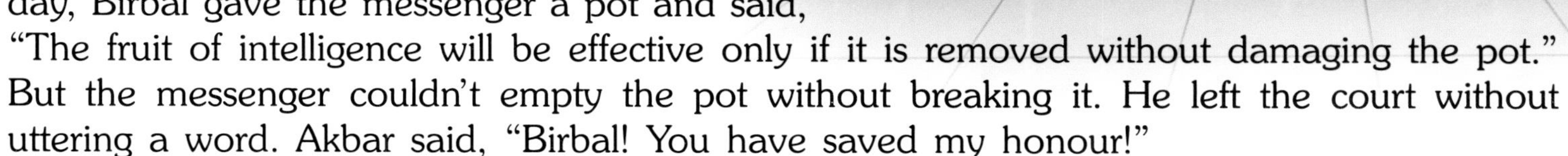

65. *The Brahmin's Wife*

There lived a short-tempered Brahmin in Akbar's kingdom. One day, he found a strand of hair in his food and shouted at his wife, "This should never happen again, or I shall punish you!" After a week, the Brahmin found a strand of hair in his food. "Enough! Your hair shall be shaved today!" he said, and rushed to bring home a barber. The Brahmin's wife and her brother went to Birbal for help. Birbal said, "Arrange for some wood." Then he whispered in the brother's ear. They went to the Brahmin's house and began making a pyre. Just then, the Brahmin arrived with the barber. The brother caught hold of the Brahmin and laid him on the pyre. The Brahmin screamed, "I am not a dead body!" Birbal said, "According to Hindu custom, the wife's hair can be shaved only after her husband has died." The Brahmin cried, "I'm sorry! I shall control my anger."

66. *God is Just and Kind*

One day, Akbar said to Birbal, "We say God is kind, but sometimes I feel God is unfair. Many are blessed with good health, while many are ill. Some are poor; some are rich. If God is our father, why does He treat His children differently?" Birbal explained, "Your Majesty, if all was well, who would pray to God? You, as our ruler, are like a father to us. You reward someone if they do good and punish those who are wicked. If someone works less, they earn less, but if they work more, you pay them more." Akbar said, "Yes, that is true." Birbal continued, "Similarly, God rewards those who are good and punishes those who do wrong deeds. Every man's fate is decided by his own actions. God is just. He always showers His blessings upon every living being and protects everyone." Akbar said, "You are right, Birbal!"

67. *The Old King's Request*

Akbar's kingdom was famous for its beauty and grandeur. One day, a messenger from a distant land came to Akbar's court. He said, "Our king sends his greetings. He wants to visit your kingdom. But our king is old. He wants to know the number of turns in the streets of your kingdom as he doesn't want to lose his way." Akbar said, "I welcome your king to my kingdom. As for the number of turns, it will take a month to count them all. I will send word to your king after it is done." The messenger said, "Your Majesty! If I go back without your answer, my king will punish me. I can wait until tomorrow." Akbar asked the messenger to go and rest. Then he called Birbal. Birbal said, "Your Majesty, every street in the world has only two turns — left turn and right turn." Once again, Birbal saved the court's honour.

68. *The Puzzle*

Akbar and Birbal shared a close relationship which had its share of strange twists. There were times when Akbar would get angry with Birbal and banish him from the court. During one such incident, Birbal went away. Akbar's soldiers searched for Birbal, but in vain. Akbar knew Birbal could not resist challenges. So he announced a puzzle which only Birbal could solve. He sent his messengers with a proposal for the neighbouring kings. The proposal read, "Emperor Akbar wishes to get the sea of his kingdom married. Send the rivers of your kingdom to him. He shall choose the best match." There came a reply from a kingdom near by. It read, "We shall send our rivers, but the wells of your kingdom should receive them." Akbar knew it was Birbal's answer. He sent his men to the kingdom with a message for Birbal to come home. Soon, they were reunited.

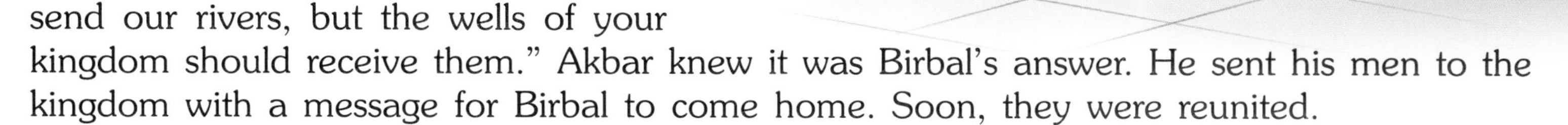

69. *Counting Sparrows*

One day, a messenger from a neighbouring kingdom came to Akbar's court. The king had sent many gifts for Akbar and Birbal. The messenger gave them the gifts and said, "My king has heard about Birbal's wit. He wants to test Birbal. He has a question for Birbal." Akbar said, "Go ahead. Birbal shall never disappoint." The messenger asked Birbal, "How many sparrows live in Agra?" Akbar was worried. But Birbal replied, "The exact number is 88,457." The messenger said, "What if there are more sparrows?" Birbal said, "That would mean some of them are entertaining their relatives from another city." The messenger pressed further, "What if there are fewer sparrows?" "Simple. Some of them have flown out of Agra to visit their relatives who live in other cities. I am sure about the number. You can count the birds anytime you want." Everyone laughed heartily. The messenger praised Birbal and left.

70. *The Skinny Goat*

Akbar and Birbal had just finished having a lavish meal. Birbal said, "Pardon me, Your Majesty! But I think you are becoming fat." Akbar said, "It's because of all the rich food the cooks serve every day." Birbal said, "No, Your Majesty. It is because you have no worries. A well-fed person with worries can never gain weight." Akbar said, "Birbal, even animals gain weight if they are fed well." Birbal wanted to prove his point. So he bought a goat. The goat was fed well twice a day. After a month Akbar came to see the goat. The goat had not gained weight. He asked Birbal "Was the goat being fed regularly?" Birbal replied, "Your Majesty, it was fed well twice a day. However, I had tied the goat to a lion's cage. Since it lived in constant fear of losing its life, it remained thin." Akbar said, "Birbal, you are right!"

71. *A Rare Gem*

Once, an ambassador from a neighbouring kingdom visited Akbar. Akbar said, "Be my guest." The ambassador had brought many gifts with him and he gave them to Akbar and his courtiers. Then he said to Akbar, "There are many alchemists in our country. They can turn any metal into gold. Our country also has many rare gemstones. What is the speciality of your kingdom?" Akbar said, "My kingdom has the rarest of rare gems, which can solve any problem." The ambassador said, "Can I see the gem?" Akbar said, "Of course!" He pointed to Birbal and said, "That's our most precious gem. He can pick out good people among many bad ones. He has solved many people's problems and saved many innocent lives. He is kind and intelligent, yet humble." The ambassador said, "You are lucky to have him." Akbar was happy with the ambassador and gave him many gifts.

72. *The Money Box*

Once, there was an old miser in Akbar's kingdom. He had a wooden box in which he kept all his money. One day, the miser's hut caught fire. He rushed outside and cried, "My money box! Please save it!" One of his neighbours said, "I shall save it, but I will only give you what I desire and keep the rest." The miser agreed. The neighbour brought the wooden box and said, "I will give you what I desire and keep the rest. I am going to keep all the money." Birbal was passing by and the miser told him about the incident. Birbal asked the neighbour to return the money box. The neighbour said, "I will give him what I desire and keep the rest." Birbal quipped, "You desire the money inside the box and therefore you will give it to the miser." The neighbour returned all the money without further ado.

73. *Endless Love*

Akbar knew a lot about many religions and was always eager to learn more. Once, he asked Birbal, "Why did Lord Krishna rush to help his devotees? Didn't He have servants? Birbal said, "I shall answer that tomorrow, Your Majesty." Then he ordered a craftsman to make a wax idol of Prince Khurram, Akbar's grandson. Next day, Akbar and Birbal were strolling in the royal garden. As they walked by the pond, Birbal signalled to the servant. The servant pushed the wax idol into the pond. Akbar thought his grandson was about to be drowned so he dived into the pond. When he grabbed the idol, he realised he was mistaken. Birbal said, "Your Majesty, why didn't you ask your servants to save Khurram?" "Could I have waited for a servant to save him?" asked Akbar. "Similarly, Lord Krishna loves His devotees so much that He does not wait for His servants to help them," explained Birbal.

74. *The Greedy Man*

Once, there lived a sage in Akbar's kingdom. An old lady came to him and said, "Please keep my life's savings with you until I return." The sage said, "I stay away from wealth. Bury them in a corner of my hut." The old lady did so and left. She came back after many months. Then she dug in the place where she had buried the coins, but they had gone. She asked Birbal for help. Birbal whispered a plan. Next day, Birbal went to the sage and said, "Please keep these jewels until I return from my cousin's house." Just then, the old lady entered. The sage wanted to impress Birbal and steal the jewels. So, he said, "Your savings are in the northern corner, lady. Take them." After the old lady had dug out her coins, a servant told Birbal that his cousin had come to visit him. Birbal took the jewels and left.

75. *A Handful of Nuts*

Once, Akbar and his courtiers were discussing the qualities of generosity and kindness. Akbar said, "The hand of the giver is always above that of the receiver." Everyone in the court pondered over the thought and agreed with him. However, Birbal said, "I do not agree with you, Your Majesty. The hand of the giver is not above that of the receiver in all cases." Akbar thought, 'Birbal is my favourite, but sometimes he thinks he knows too much.' Then, he asked, "Birbal, tell me when the hand of the receiver is above that of the giver." Birbal said, "Wait a minute, Your Majesty," and left the court. Soon, he returned with a handful of nuts. He offered them to the emperor and said, "The hand of the receiver is above that of the giver when someone offers nuts." Akbar smiled. He thought, 'Birbal has extraordinary presence of mind.'

76. *The Emperor's Touch*

One day, an old lady visited Birbal. She was in tears. Birbal asked, "What happened?" The old lady said, "I had a son who died in battle and I am all alone." Birbal wiped her tears and said, "Do you have anything to give the emperor?" The old lady said, "Yes, my son's sword. Birbal said, "Give it to the emperor; he will surely give you something." The old lady met Akbar and said, "Your Majesty, my son is no more. I've brought his sword to you so that it may be used again." Akbar said, "The sword is rusted. It is useless." He ordered the servant to give the lady a few coins. Birbal said, "Your Majesty, I have heard everything turns into gold with your touch. Why not this sword?" Akbar asked his servants to weigh the sword and gave the old lady gold coins equal to its weight. The old lady was happy.

77. *The River's Tears*

One evening, Akbar and Birbal were walking along the banks of the Yamuna. Akbar loved the sound of the flowing river. He told Birbal, "Listen to the river, Birbal. I feel it is crying. Can you tell me why it is crying?" Birbal stared at the river for a while. He thought, 'This is a strange question, but I must give a sensible answer.' Then he said, "Your Majesty, the mountain is the father of the river. The sea is her husband. When the river flows down from the mountain, she is sad to leave her father behind to meet her husband. She must flow on and she cannot stop even though she loves her father. That's why she is always crying." Akbar marvelled at the thought and said, "How beautiful, Birbal! Here, take this bracelet as a reward." Birbal was happy that his answer had pleased Akbar.

78. *Tit for Tat*

Akbar had a special cupboard. Whoever touched the cupboard would get stuck to it. One day, Akbar called Birbal and said, "Please get me an apple from that cupboard." When Birbal touched the cupboard, he got stuck. Try as he might, he couldn't free himself. Then onwards, Akbar often teased Birbal. He would ask, "How was the ghost of the apple?" One day, when Akbar went hunting, Birbal hid in the forest. As luck would have it, Akbar got separated from his soldiers. Suddenly, a ghost appeared in front of him. Akbar fainted. Akbar's soldiers found him and took him to the palace. Akbar did not breathe a word about the incident. The next time when Akbar teased Birbal, "How was the ghost of the apple?" Birbal asked, "How was the ghost of the forest?" Akbar realised that Birbal had scared him in the forest. He never teased Birbal again.

79. *The Hospitable Relatives*

One day, Birbal decided to visit his relatives in another city. He set off on his carriage. Birbal's relatives were not hospitable people. They did not like to entertain guests. When they saw Birbal's carriage approaching, they quickly thought of a plan to send him away. They went to the balcony and pretended to have a fight. They began shouting at each other. Birbal knew his relatives were pretending to fight so that he might go away. Birbal pretended to go away. He left his carriage outside their lane and went near the house. He hid behind some bushes. The couple had stopped fighting. He overheard them saying, "Well done! Birbal has gone away!" Just then, Birbal jumped from behind the bushes and said, "I haven't gone! I was pretending, too!" The couple was ashamed. They turned over a new leaf and always welcomed their guests.

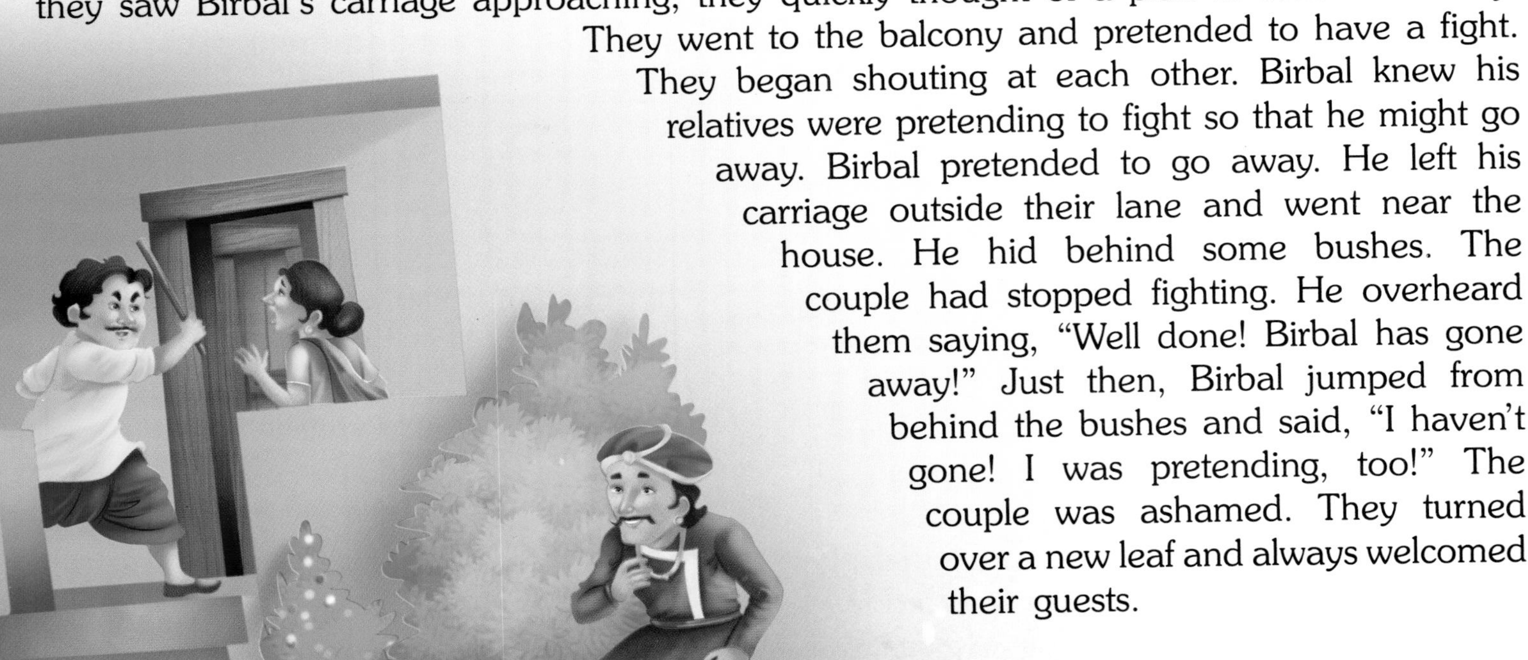

80. *The Candlestick Collection*

Akbar had a habit of collecting beautiful candlesticks. He had a special chamber where his collection was displayed. The servants were given strict instructions to be careful while cleaning the room. One day, while a servant was dusting the mantelpiece, one of the candlesticks fell and broke. Akbar was beside himself with rage. He ordered his guards to hang the servant. Birbal wanted to save the servant. He whispered his plan to the servant. Next day, a soldier asked the servant about his last wish. The servant said, "I will tell the emperor about it." When he was taken to Akbar, he bowed before him and said, "Your Majesty, my last wish is to break all the candlesticks." Akbar was surprised. "Why?" he thundered. "I want to save all the other servants from death in case a candlestick breaks accidentally." Akbar realised his mistake and set the servant free.

81. *A Touch of Sweetness*

One day, Birbal saw his neighbour, Raghuram, yelling at a fortune-teller, asking him to go away. Birbal asked the fortune-teller, "Why did he drive you out?" The fortune-teller said, "I asked him to stop being greedy as that would lead to his downfall. I advised him to donate alms to the poor. How could I hide the bitter truth?" "We shall offer him a dose of sweet truth," said Birbal, and whispered his plan. Next day, the fortune-teller walked by Raghuram's house, disguised as an old man. Raghuram welcomed him. After studying his palm, the fortune-teller said, "You are fortunate, son! If you give alms to the poor, you will be highly prosperous!" Raghuram was happy with what he heard. He gave the fortune-teller a bag of gold coins. The fortune-teller met Birbal and said, "Thank you for teaching me that more than the truth, it's how you present it. That matters a lot."

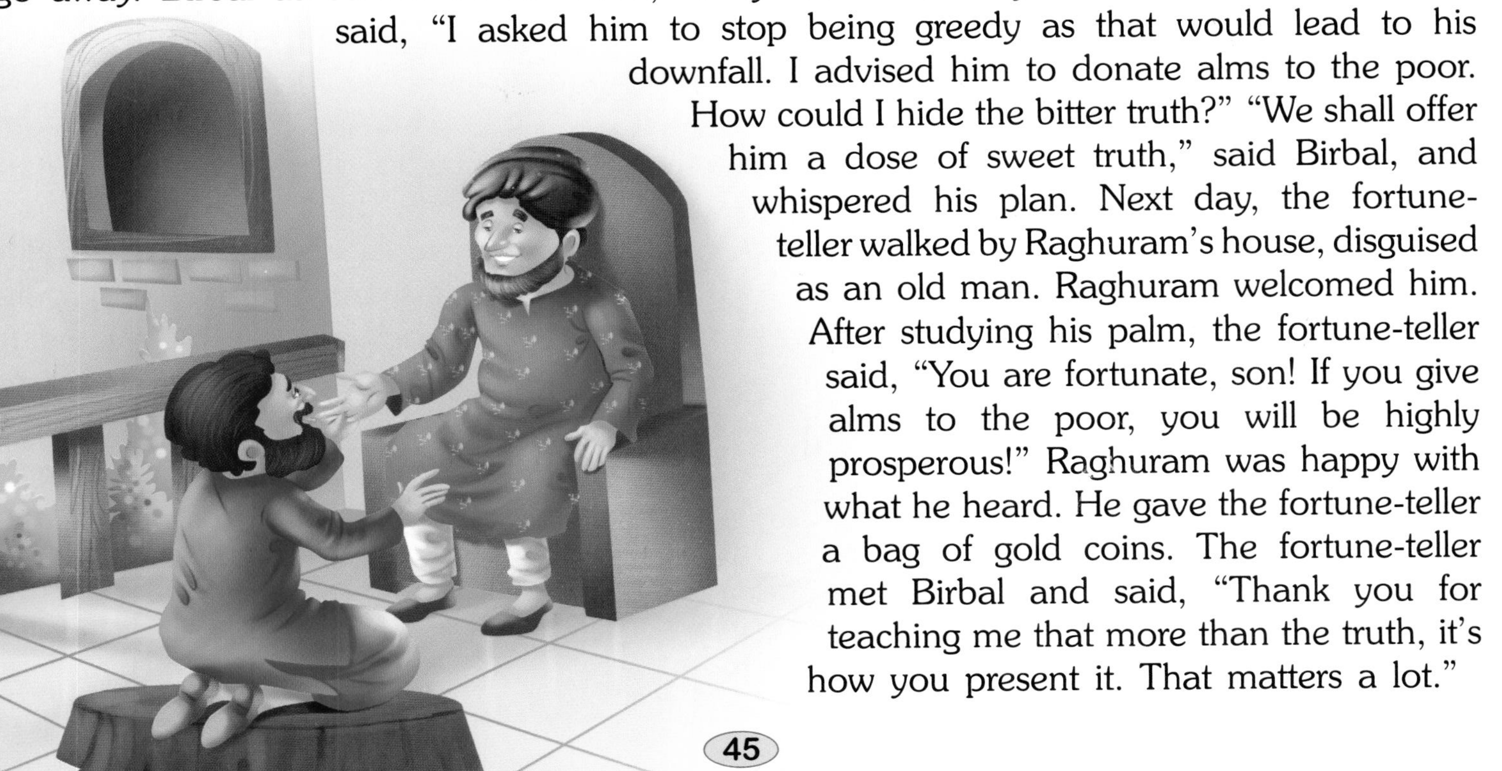

82. *As You Sow, So Shall You Reap*

Akbar had a courtier named Sultan. He wanted his son to become the royal treasurer. But Akbar and Birbal did not want this, as Sultan's son was a rogue. Sultan thought, 'If I turn the emperor against Birbal, my son can become the royal treasurer.' One day, Birbal was late for the court. Sultan whispered to Akbar, "Your Majesty, Birbal is becoming careless day by day. Punish him." Akbar knew about Sultan's intentions, but he asked, "How?" Sultan said, "Say 'no' to all that Birbal asks." Birbal said, "I am sorry; my wife is ill. I had taken her to the doctor." Akbar replied, "No, I don't believe you." Birbal saw Sultan smiling and understood what had happened. Birbal asked, "Shall we discuss work?" Akbar replied, "No." Birbal asked, "May I go home?" Akbar said, "No." Then Birbal asked, "Will you appoint Sultan's son as the royal treasurer?" Akbar said, "No," and winked at Birbal.

83. *Royal Fishermen*

One day, Akbar's guards brought a man to the court and said, "Your Majesty, this granary officer was caught taking bribes." Akbar said, "Put him in prison." Another courtier said, "Your Majesty, let him count the waves of the Yamuna." Akbar agreed. After a few days, Akbar asked Birbal, "What about that corrupt granary officer? Is he still taking bribes?" Birbal said, "Your Majesty, we won't know unless we find out for ourselves." Akbar and Birbal disguised themselves as fishermen and were walking on the banks of the Yamuna, when the officer saw them. "What are you doing here?" he roared. "Sir, we are poor fishermen. We have come to cast our nets." "Well, you cannot. You disturbed me while I was performing an important task. Pay me a fine of two hundred coins. Akbar said, "You will be jailed for this!" Akbar's guards caught the officer and imprisoned him.

84. *The White Elephants*

One day, a washerman's donkey broke the pitchers of his neighbour, a potter. The washerman paid for the broken pitchers. The potter accepted the money. But he was wicked. So he went to Akbar and said, "Your Majesty, I had a guest from a distant country. The elephants in that country are clean and white." Akbar said, "I shall ask all the washermen to bathe my elephants." The potter said, "My neighbour, the washerman, can do a great job!" The washerman asked Birbal, "No matter how much I clean, the elephants will not turn white. What shall I do?" Birbal whispered his plan. Next day, the washerman told Akbar, "If the potter gives me a huge pot to bathe the elephants, I can make them white." The potter made a huge pot. But it broke when the elephant stepped into it. Akbar thundered, "Make a strong pot!" The potter apologised and begged Akbar for forgiveness.

85. *Angry Words*

One day, Akbar caught a dishonest officer cheating his subjects. He was angry and upset. Just then, his servant told him, "Your Majesty's horse has run away from its stable and I cannot find it anywhere." Akbar said, "You deserve to die!" The servant trembled from head to toe. Birbal saw this and he knew this was not fair. So he said, "Your Majesty, the horse has run away and it will come back sooner or later, but the servant's life will be gone forever. Please pardon him." Akbar said, "Birbal, when I am angry I will only do the opposite of what needs to be done." Birbal immediately said, "Your Majesty, you are right. This servant is a careless man who cannot find your horse. It is good that you have punished him with a death sentence." Akbar realised that he had spoken in anger and pardoned the servant.

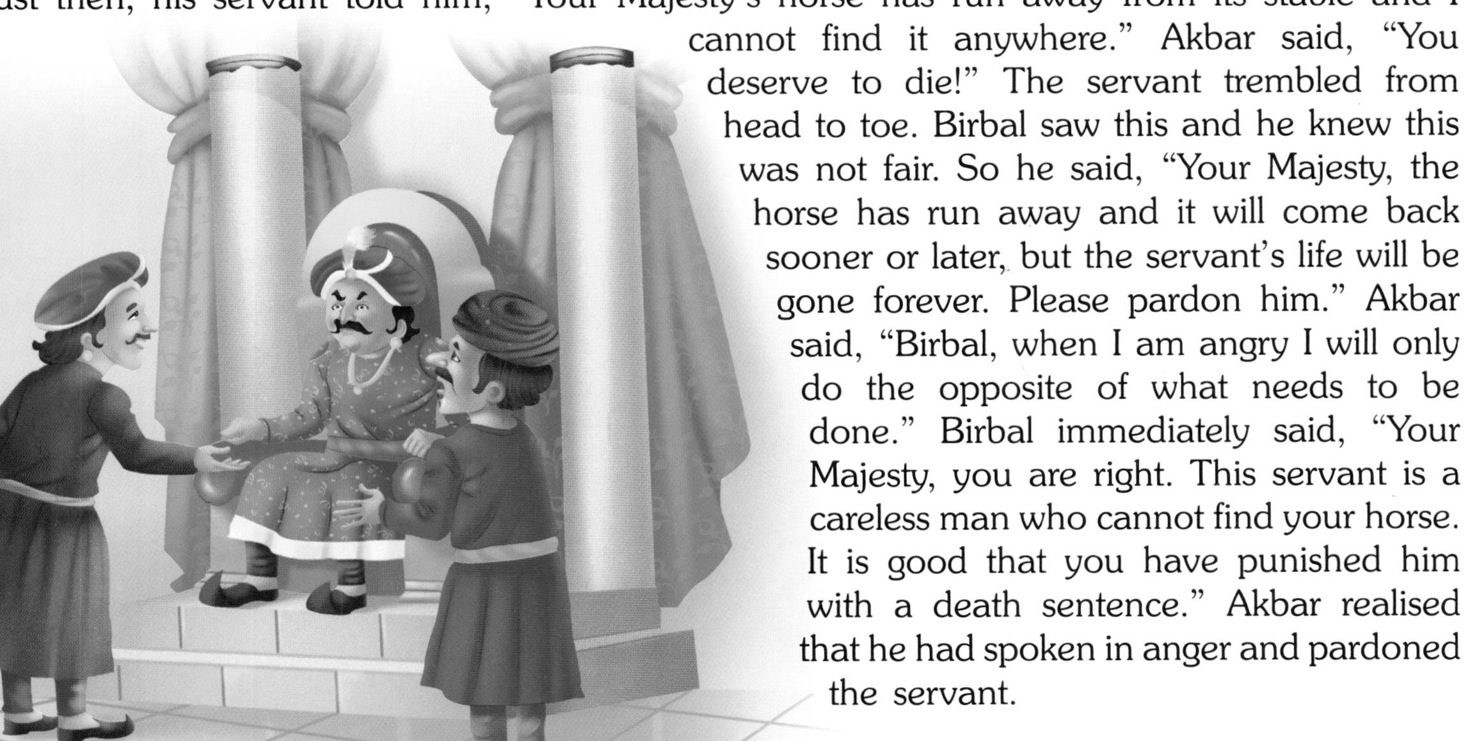

86. *A Sweet Act*

Akbar enjoyed asking his courtiers strange questions to test their intelligence. One day, he asked, "How should I treat a person who pulls my moustache?" All the courtiers were taken aback. After a while, one of them said, "Your Majesty, such a person should be in jail." Another courtier said, "No, Your Majesty, such a person should be beaten." But other courtiers disagreed and said, Your Majesty, how dare someone pull your moustache? Such a person deserves a death sentence." Birbal was listening to everyone. Just then, Akbar asked, "Birbal, what do you think?" "Your Majesty! Such a person should be given sweets," said Birbal with a smile. Akbar was surprised. He said, "Birbal, why do you say this?" Birbal said, "Yes, Your Majesty! None can pull your moustache, except your grandson. So he should be given sweets." Everyone laughed out loud. Birbal always spread happiness with his positive thinking.

87. *The Pots of Ghee*

Birbal was a clever man. Not only did he save innocent lives, but he also solved many problems and caught dishonest people. One day, two ghee merchants came to Akbar's court. The first merchant said, "Your Majesty, this man had borrowed money from me. After a few months, I asked him to return the money. But he denied having borrowed any money." The second merchant said, "Your Majesty, I haven't taken any money." Birbal came up with a plan to catch the cheat between them. He asked his servants to fill two pots with ghee. He placed two gold coins in each pot and gave it to them. "Weigh these pots and give them back," he said. The first merchant returned the pot with the gold coin. However, the second merchant returned the pot of ghee without the gold coin. Birbal found out that the second merchant was dishonest and punished him.

88. *Birbal, the Irreplaceable*

One day, Hussain, one of Akbar's courtiers, told him, "Birbal has been your trusted courtier for long. Please give me a chance." Akbar replied, "You must prove yourself. Accompany Birbal to Burma and give my letter to the king." Birbal and Hussain left for Burma. Birbal gave the letter to the king, who read it and said, "Akbar wants me to hang you on a full-moon night." Birbal whispered his plan to Hussain. The king treated them graciously until the fateful night. On the full-moon night, Hussain said, "Hang me first." Birbal said, "No, hang me first." The king asked, "Why are you so eager to die?" Birbal answered, "Whoever is hanged first will be reborn as the King of Burma." The king was petrified. He sent them back to Akbar. Akbar asked, "Hussain, are you ready to replace Birbal?" Hussain said, "No, Your Majesty. Birbal is very intelligent. He is irreplaceable."

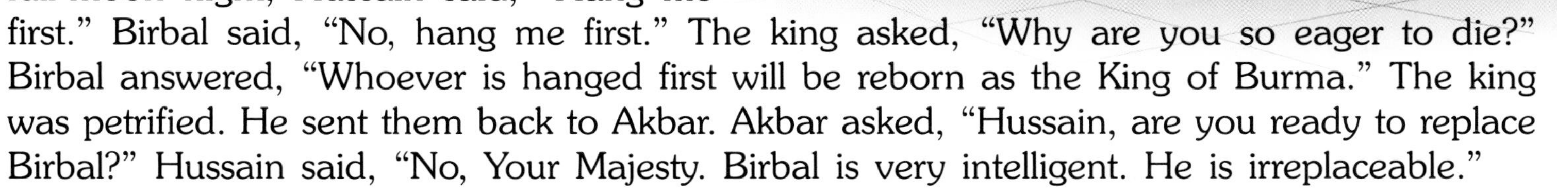

89. *The Gift of Eid*

It is a well-known fact that Akbar was a generous king. On the eve of Eid, he announced, "Eid is a time to enjoy with friends and family. Hence, tomorrow is a holiday. Enjoy the festival with your loved ones. But, before you leave, pick a gift." He pointed to a table, which was heaped with expensive gifts. The courtiers thanked Akbar and rushed towards the table. But Birbal stayed behind. When everyone had taken their pick and left, Birbal went towards the table. Only one gift remained — a silver platter. He picked it up and covered it with a piece of cloth. Akbar asked, "Why did you cover it? Don't you like it?" Birbal said, "Your Majesty, if I carry an empty platter, people will say your riches have decreased." Akbar said, "Birbal! You always think about me first." He took off his pearl necklace and put it on Birbal's silver platter.

90. *The Golden Peacock*

One day, the royal guards brought a bird catcher into Akbar's court. The man said, "Your Majesty, I have a beautiful gift for you. I hope you will accept it." Akbar said, "Certainly. What is it?" The man brought in a cage, with a golden peacock in it. All the courtiers gasped in wonder. None of them had seen a golden peacock. Akbar said, "I am very happy, young man! You shall be rewarded tomorrow." But Birbal was suspicious. He wanted to find out where the golden peacock had come from. Next day, when Akbar was rewarding the bird catcher, Birbal said, "Your Majesty, please wait. I know a man who is better than this bird catcher." Akbar was surprised. Birbal brought in a poor man and said, "Your Majesty, this is the artist who paints ordinary birds into wonderful creatures. Akbar rewarded the artist and punished the bird catcher.

91. *The Lazy Courtier*

One day, some villagers entered Akbar's court. They bowed before Akbar and said, "Your Majesty, we will die of thirst. There are no wells in our village. Every day, we travel to the neighbouring village to bring water. Please help us!" Akbar thought, 'I had ordered a courtier to get wells dug all over my kingdom. What happened?' Then he sent one of his courtiers to inspect the village. Next day, the courtier said, "The wells are disappearing from the village, Your Majesty." Akbar asked, "How is that possible?" Birbal said, "Your Majesty, let's go there and see for ourselves." Akbar and Birbal went on a tour of the kingdom and found that the courtier who was appointed to dig wells was lazing around and bossing over the villagers. Akbar said, "Birbal, see to it that wells are dug all over the kingdom." Then he banished the lazy courtier.

92. *The Money Mirage*

There lived a poor Brahmin in Akbar's kingdom. One night, he had a strange dream. He dreamt that his friend gave him some money. The Brahmin met his friend the next morning and told him about this dream. The friend who heard that he had lent the money to the Brahmin was a cunning man. He said, "Return the money that I had given you." The Brahmin said, "But it was just a dream." The friend said, "I want my money." The Brahmin and his friend approached Birbal for help. Birbal asked the friend, "So you want the money you gave your friend in the dream." He replied, "Yes." Birbal asked a servant to bring a mirror. He placed some money in front of the mirror and said, "Can you see the money?" The cunning man replied, "Yes Sir." Birbal said, "All your money has been returned to you."

93. *Unflinching Faith*

One day, Akbar's courtiers were discussing about God. Birbal said, "Whatever God does is for the ultimate good of everyone." A courtier asked, "I lost my toe in an accident. How is it good for me?" Birbal said, "Only God knows His ways. Time will prove that I am right." A few days later, Akbar and his courtiers went hunting. The courtier who had lost his toe wandered deep into the forest. Suddenly, some tribesmen caught him and took him to their chief. The chief said, "Tie him up. Let's sacrifice him to our deity." Just then, one of them noticed that the courtier's toe was missing. The chief said, "Release him! We cannot sacrifice him." Tired and hungry, he was searching for a way out of the forest when he reunited with Akbar and his courtiers. When he told them what had happened, they admired Birbal for his faith in God.

94. *A Strange Task*

Once, some of Akbar's courtiers who were jealous of Birbal told Akbar, "Your Majesty, if Birbal can do anything and everything, he can also bring you the milk of an ox." Akbar asked Birbal to do so. Birbal went home and told his plan to his daughter. At night, Birbal's daughter went to the royal well and began washing clothes noisily. When the royal guards asked her what she was doing, she kept quiet. So they took her to Akbar. Akbar asked her, "Why are you washing clothes at night?" Birbal's daughter said, "Your Majesty, my father gave birth to a baby. I'm washing these clothes for the baby to wear." Akbar asked, "How can Birbal give birth?" The child replied, "If an ox can give milk, why can't a man give birth?" Akbar knew she was Birbal's daughter. He sent her home and said, "Tell Birbal I don't need the ox's milk."

95. *The Merchant's Pet*

One day, two merchants named Dhanamal and Sonamal came to Akbar's court. Akbar asked, "What is the matter?" Dhanamal said, "Your Majesty, I had borrowed money from Sonamal and promised to return it within a week. Dhanamal told me that I would have to give him the flesh of my pet peacock if I couldn't return the money within a week. After three days, I repaid the money, but Sonamal refused the money. After a week had passed, Sonamal came to me and asked for the piece of flesh. I love my pet. Please help me." Akbar asked Birbal to solve the problem. Birbal told Sonamal, "You mentioned the peacock's flesh, but you said nothing about blood. You may take a piece of flesh, but not a drop of blood." Everyone knew this was an impossible task. Akbar punished Sonamal and asked him to pay a fine for refusing the money returned by Dhanamal.

96. *The Parrots' Wedding*

Akbar was very fond of hunting. He would frequently go on hunting expeditions. Slowly, the animals of the forest were decreasing. Birbal was worried. He wanted to let the emperor know that it was wrong to kill animals and birds for pleasure. The next time Akbar went hunting, Birbal accompanied him. Once in the forest, Birbal pretended to know the language of birds. When they passed by a huge banyan tree, they heard a group of parrots chirping loudly. Akbar asked Birbal what they were saying. Birbal said, "They are discussing marriage plans. The groom's father is asking for five forests that have no animals in them." "Go on," said Akbar. "The bride's father says he can give not five, but ten empty forests. He says the king of this land is so fond of hunting that he can arrange for more, if needed." Akbar was shocked. He stopped hunting from that day on.

97. *Little Lies*

One day, Akbar said to Birbal, "Lying is bad. There are people who tell lies many times in their lives. I have neither told a lie in my life nor will I ever do so." Birbal said, "Your Majesty, sometimes we lie to avoid hurting someone." Akbar said, "I don't think so. I will never lie." After some days, Birbal told Akbar, "Your Majesty, God appeared in my house and said He wants to meet the person with the purest heart. I said it can be none other than you. Let's go." Akbar was pleased. He went to Birbal's house. Birbal pointed to the place of worship and said, "There, Your Majesty." But Akbar couldn't see God. 'What a shame!' he thought. But he told Birbal that he had seen God. Birbal smiled mischievously. Akbar asked, "God didn't appear in front of you, did He? Birbal, you made me lie!"

98. *Winsome Ways*

Once, the king of a neighbouring country invited Birbal to his palace. The king had heard a lot about Birbal's wisdom. He was jealous of Birbal and was rude to him. But Birbal bore everything with a smile. Some time later, the king's guards told him, "An old beggar has entered the royal garden!" The king went there. The old beggar had just finished planting a mango sapling. The king asked, "Why did you plant the sapling here? By the time the tree bears fruit, you will certainly be dead." The beggar replied, "I planted it so that you and your children might enjoy its fruit." The king was touched. He said, "Come, I shall reward you." The beggar took off his beard and wig, and lo! It was Birbal! The king was ashamed of himself. Birbal had done a good deed in turn for a bad deed and won over the king.

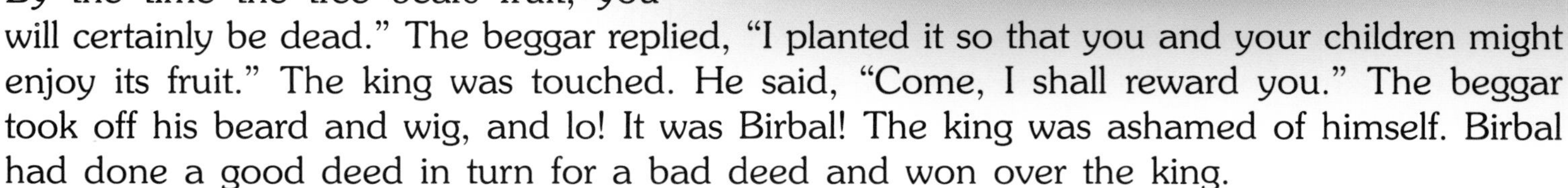

99. *The Speaking Tree*

Once, an old man and his neighbour went to Birbal. The old man said, "I gave my valuables to my neighbour before going on a pilgrimage. I am back, but my neighbour refuses to return them." The neighbour said, "This man never gave me any valuables." Birbal asked the old man, "Does anyone else know about this?" The old man said, "No. We were standing under a tree." Birbal said, "Bring the tree here." The old man went away. Birbal asked the neighbour, "Where is that tree? Will he return soon?" The neighbour replied, "The tree is far off. He will take time to return." After a long time, the old man returned. "The tree wouldn't budge," he said. Birbal said, "While you were away, the tree told us the truth." "When?" asked the neighbour. "Just when you said that the tree is far," said Birbal. The neighbour returned the old man's valuables.

100. *A Case of Nothing*

Once, two men rushed to Birbal for help. One of them was a poor man. He had a bundle of clothes on his head. He said, "Sir, I was walking in the hot sun with the bundle of clothes. I was tired, so I took the load off my head and rested under a tree." "And then?" asked Birbal. "I asked this man to help me place the bundle on my head. He asked me what I would pay him. I said 'nothing'. He helped me, but now he wants the 'nothing' that I mentioned." Birbal told the other man, "I shall pay you on behalf of this poor man. Come with me." Birbal led him to a room. He said, "See, there is something under the chair." The man said, "Sir! There is nothing under the chair." "Take it!" said Birbal. The cunning man realised his mistake.

101. *No Child's Play*

Once, Akbar could not start an important meeting because Birbal was late. When Birbal finally arrived, Akbar was angry with him. "Birbal! Why are you late?" he thundered. "Your Majesty, my child was crying. I was trying to calm him down," replied Birbal. Akbar said, "You don't know anything about children." Birbal replied, "Your Majesty, why don't you teach me?" Akbar said, "You are the child. I am the father." Birbal began crying. Akbar asked, "What do you want?" Birbal said, "Father! I want a cow." Akbar ordered for a cow. Birbal cried again. "What is it, child?" asked Akbar. Birbal said, "I want milk!" Akbar ordered his servants to milk the cow. Birbal drank a little bit of milk and began crying again. "What happened?" asked Akbar. "Put the milk back in the cow!" said Birbal. Akbar gave up. He understood that bringing up a child was not easy.

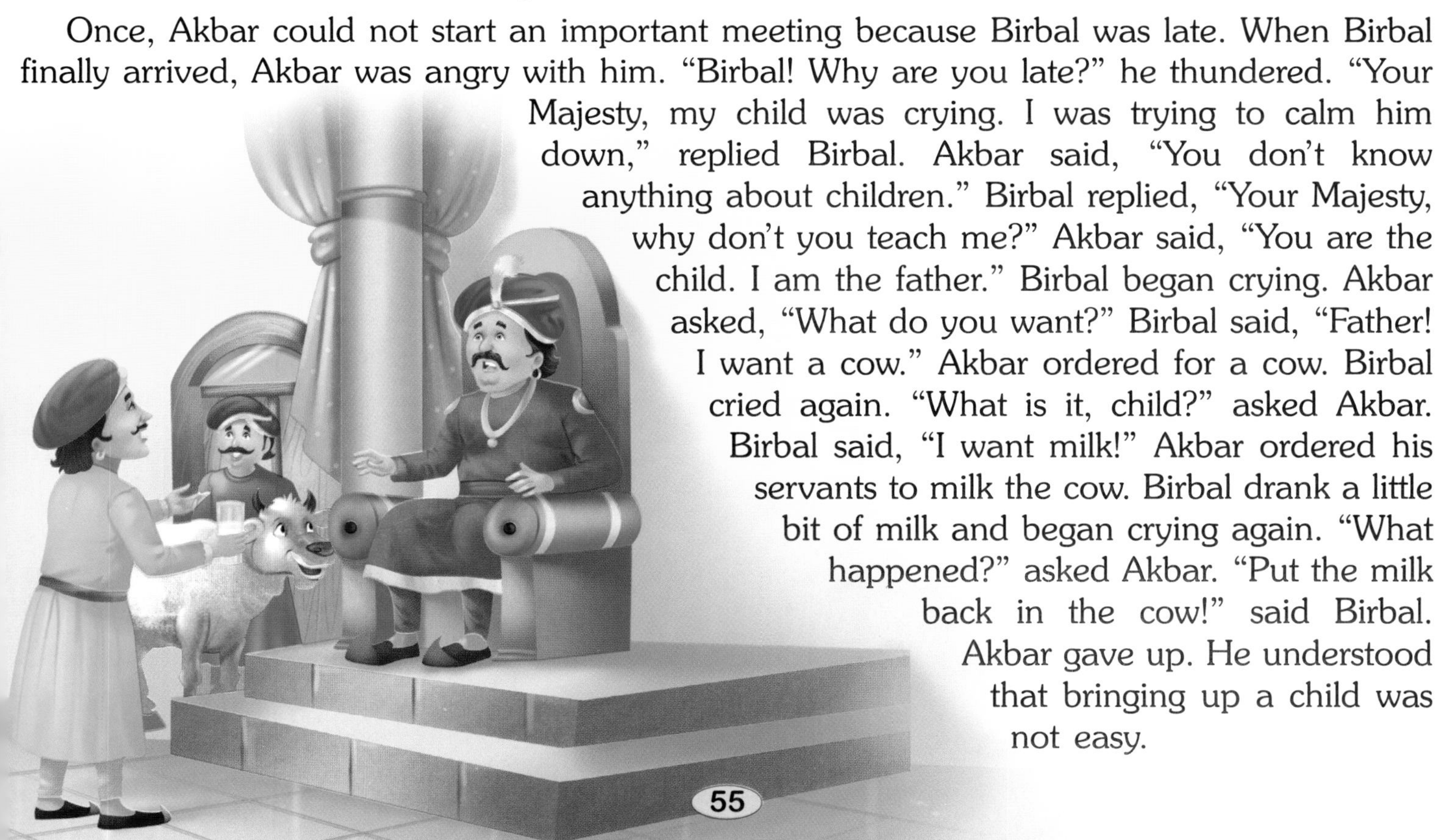

102. *The Gardener's Gold*

One day, the royal gardener went to Birbal and said, "Sir, someone has stolen my gold coins! I had hidden them under the pear tree." Birbal asked, "Had anyone seen you hiding it?" The gardener said "Nobody else knew about it." Birbal called the royal doctor and asked, "Have you treated anybody with medicines made from the root of a pear tree?" He said, "Yes, I had treated a merchant with its roots a few days ago. I had asked the merchant's servant to get the roots." Birbal sent a messenger, asking him to bring the servant to Akbar's court. When the servant arrived, Birbal asked him about the gold coins. The servant said, "Sir, I found the gold coins near the roots of the tree. Had I known they belonged to someone, I wouldn't have cast a second glance at them." He returned the gold coins to the gardener.

103. *Curry Confusion*

One night, Birbal was invited to a grand feast. Next day, during lunch, Akbar asked, "How was the feast, Birbal?" Birbal described the lavish feast and listed the items that were served. He had to stop when a courtier entered with a message for the emperor. In the court, Akbar asked, "What else, Birbal?" Birbal's eyes twinkled with mischief. He replied, "Curry, Your Majesty!" Akbar laughed heartily as he was pleased with Birbal's wit. He gave Birbal a necklace studded with rubies. The other courtiers thought curry was Akbar's favourite dish. They went home and asked their wives to prepare delicious curry. Next day, Akbar was greeted with bowls of curry. Akbar asked, "What is all this?" The courtiers replied, "We know you love curry. That's why you gifted Birbal a necklace." Akbar said, "You are fools. You don't know why Birbal said 'curry'. Next time, think before you act and stop copying others!"

104. *The Terrific Turban*

Akbar praised Birbal a lot and this did not go down well with some jealous courtiers. Mulla was one of them. One day, when Birbal entered the court wearing a classy turban, Akbar said, "Your turban looks very good on you. It has been tied so neatly!" But before Birbal could reply, Mulla interrupted, "Your Majesty! There's nothing special about his turban. I can tie my turban in a better way." Akbar said, "Very well! Wear your best turban tomorrow!" Next day, everyone looked dashing in his turban. Mulla also wore a nice turban. Akbar said, "Mulla, you look handsome today. Your turban has been tied so neatly!" Just then, Birbal said, "Your Majesty, "Mulla's turban looks terrific. But he cannot win the challenge because he has taken help from his wife in tying the turban." Everyone laughed at this remark. Mulla was silent. He understood that he was no match for Birbal.

105. *The Birthday Gift*

It was the birthday of the emperor himself. The whole kingdom was bubbling with joy. Kings from faraway lands, ministers and courtiers filled the palace with the finest of gifts. But Akbar's mind was elsewhere. His eyes were searching for his most precious gem — Birbal. One courtier told Akbar, "Your Majesty, everyone has arrived, except Birbal." After a few hours, when the crowd had started thinning, Birbal arrived with a box. He said, "Your Majesty, may God bless you! Here are my best wishes!" Akbar asked, "What took you so long?" "I was choosing your gift," he said, and he handed over the box. Akbar immediately unwrapped and opened the box. It was a flowering plant." Akbar said, "What pretty flowers! How do you know I like these?" Birbal smiled and said, "We had gone for a walk one evening when you praised these flowers." "How thoughtful! This is the best gift I've received!" said Akbar.

106. *The Fearless*

One day, Akbar asked, "Who is the most fearless person in this world?" All the courtiers except Birbal, replied, "Of course, it's you, Your Majesty!" Since Birbal was quiet, Akbar asked him, "Tell me who the bravest person in this world is." "A child, Your Majesty!" said Birbal. Everyone was surprised with Birbal's answer. "Prove it," said Akbar. "Certainly, Your Majesty!" said Birbal. Next day, Birbal brought a toddler to the court. The child was so small that he could barely walk or talk. Birbal gave the toddler to Akbar, who cuddled the child. Soon, the child began playing with Akbar. He pulled Akbar's moustache. Birbal asked Akbar, "Your Majesty, isn't a child the most fearless of all? Who else would have the courage to pull your moustache?" Akbar was very happy with Birbal's intelligence. "Well said, Birbal!" he said, and he gifted him an emerald ring.

107. *The Disappearing Valuables*

Once, an old woman and a doctor went to Akbar's court. But Birbal, as usual, solved it with his intelligence. The old woman said she was blind, while the doctor said she could see. Birbal took the old woman to another room and asked her, "What is the matter?" The old woman said, "I had called the doctor to heal my blindness. During each visit, the doctor would apply medicine on my eyes. However, he would also steal something from my house. After the doctor had stolen the valuables from my house, he healed me completely. Then he asked me for his fee. Since he had stolen my valuables, I told him I was still blind." Birbal took the old woman to Akbar and said, "The old woman is right. She is still blind; she cannot see the valuables that she had before she became blind." Akbar punished the doctor for stealing the old woman's belongings.

108. *Fun and Games*

Once, Birbal was on holiday. That day, his son told him, "Father, please come with me to the park! My friends and I want to play with you!" Birbal went with his son and began playing with all the children. After some time, a courtier passed by. He saw Birbal playing like a child among other children. He went near Birbal and said, "Birbal, I am shocked to see you here. Such pastimes do not suit your age and position." Birbal looked around the park and saw a bow. He picked it up and went to the courtier. Then he said, "Look at this bow. If it is always strained, it will lose its elasticity. We should let it free sometimes so that it may stay in use. Similarly, all work and no play will make us dull." The courtier said, "I too want to join in the fun and games!"

109. *The Wicked Robber*

One day, the royal guards brought a robber to Akbar's court and said, "Your Majesty, this man has robbed many people's gold and money." Akbar roared, "Why did you rob so many people?" The robber said, "Your Majesty, it is God's will. How can I be punished for things that were directed by God?" Birbal went near the robber and whispered, "Give me all your gold or I shall kill you." The robber immediately revealed where he had hidden all the gold. Birbal turned to Akbar and said, "This robber should be hanged, Your Majesty!" The robber cried, "Liar! I gave out the hiding place, so you would save me." Birbal replied, "It was God's will that I take your gold and get you hanged." The robber learnt his lesson. Akbar punished him for his bad deeds. Birbal returned all the gold and money to the actual owners.

110. *Freedom and Slavery*

Emperor Akbar thought Birbal was very wise. He always wanted to learn from Birbal. One day, he asked, "Birbal! Tell us something about the path to freedom and the path to slavery!" Birbal said, "Your Majesty, at the outset, the path to freedom will be full of obstacles and steep climbs. In fact, there will actually be no path, just thorns, rocks and danger all around! But after a struggle, a smooth pathway will appear all of a sudden. The pathway will be strewn with flowers. Those who put up a brave front and face all the difficulties will be happy in the end." "The path to slavery," Birbal continued, "is just the opposite. In the beginning, it will be a smooth road, without any difficulty and full of flowers. Later, there will be nothing but rocks, steep climbs and danger on all sides. It ends in sorrow." "Very well said!" Akbar exclaimed.

111. *A True Winner*

A wrestling competition was once held in the palace. Wrestlers from all over Akbar's kingdom participated in the competition. Emperor Akbar, Birbal and the other courtiers watched the competition. When it ended, the winner boasted, "I am the champion! I am the most powerful man in the country. Does anybody want to challenge me?" Birbal walked up to the wrestler and asked, "Were your competitors as strongly built as you are?" The wrestler said, "Not at all. I could easily win over them." Birbal said, "Then you are not a true winner. You shouldn't be so proud." The winner asked, "Didn't you see how I defeated everyone? Birbal replied, "One should not be proud of defeating weaker people. A competition is fair only if it takes place between the two people of equal strength." The winner understood Birbal's counsel and began teaching the art of wrestling to the weak wrestlers.

112. *The Stone Thrower*

One morning, Birbal was going to the court. A wicked man was hiding near the palace. When Birbal passed by, the man threw a stone at him. Birbal was hurt. He chased the man and caught him. Then Birbal gave the man some money. The man was surprised. He asked, "Why are you rewarding me when I have hurt you?" Birbal said, "I did not want to go to work today. You hurt me. So I got an excuse to stay at home." The wicked man was happy. He asked, "I want more money. Where can I find another man like you?" Birbal took the man near the palace and pointed towards a guard and said, "He shall pay you more if you throw a stone at him." The man threw a stone at the guard, who chained him and took him to the court to be punished.

113. *The Company He Keeps*

One day, after the usual session at the court, Akbar and Birbal were strolling in the royal garden. Birbal was talking and Akbar was listening. As they walked on, Birbal said some things that Akbar did not like. Akbar went on listening to Birbal. However, Birbal did not know that he had annoyed Akbar. As Birbal went on and on, Akbar found it difficult to keep quiet. He said, "Birbal, my patience is wearing thin." Birbal asked, "What happened, Your Majesty?" Akbar replied, "You are annoying me with your words. Although we spend a lot of time together yet I cannot go on listening to you all the time." Birbal smiled and said, "Your Majesty! Our companions affect our behaviour. I think it has to do with the company that I keep." Akbar laughed aloud. After all, Birbal's companion was Akbar himself! Once again, Birbal won Akbar's heart with his quick wit.

114. *The Best Season*

One day, Akbar asked his courtiers, "Which is the finest season?" One courtier said, "Your Majesty! It's spring, when flowers are in bloom, and the buzzing of bees and chirping of birds fills the air. "No, winter is the best," said another courtier, "when people enjoy the warm rays of the sun. Vegetables abound and we can curl up under cosy blankets." Another courtier said, "Summer is the best, Your Majesty! We can enjoy refreshments and go for long walks on pleasant evenings." Akbar asked, "What do you think, Birbal?" Birbal said, "The finest season is when a man is well fed, Your Majesty! An empty stomach knows nothing about fine weather. With a hungry stomach, the buzzing of bees in spring will sting the ears; the winter will be long and cold; and the summer sun shall burn the skin." Akbar was pleased with Birbal's concern for the common citizen.

115. *The Stolen Ring*

Occasionally, Akbar would disguise himself as a common man and walk the streets alone. Birbal would advise him to take along his guards, but Akbar never listened to him. One day, Akbar took to the streets, ignoring Birbal's advice. After a while, a bearded man started following him. Akbar asked the man, "Who are you? Where do you live?" "I am a wanderer. I can live wherever I want!" said the man. Akbar said, "How can you be rude to Emperor Akbar?" The man asked, "What is the proof?" Akbar showed him the royal ring. The man snatched it and ran away. When Akbar returned to the palace, he saw a letter on his bed, along with his ring. The letter read: 'I had warned you that it was unsafe on the streets without the guards!' Akbar realised that it was Birbal who had snatched the ring. Thereafter, he always heeded Birbal's advice.

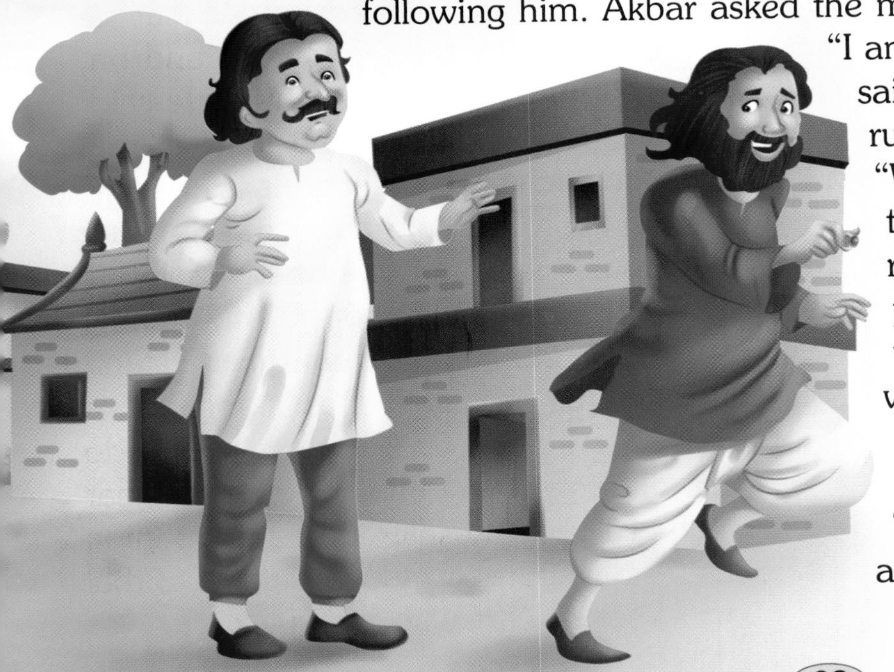

116. *The Cabbage Field*

One day, Akbar said to Birbal, "I want to know whether the farmers of my kingdom are happy. Let's go and find out." Akbar and Birbal set off on horseback. The countryside was beautiful. On the way, they came across a field of cabbages. Akbar said, "I just love cabbages. Don't you like those?" Birbal replied, "Yes, Your Majesty! It's the king of vegetables." After a few months, Akbar and Birbal decided to meet the farmers again. This time, when they passed by the field of cabbages, Akbar said, "I used to like cabbages, but I don't like those anymore!" Birbal said, "True, Your Majesty! I agree with you." Akbar said, "Birbal! I am surprised. A few months ago you said it's the king of vegetables." Birbal smiled and added, "Your Majesty, I am your servant, not the cabbage's!" Thus, Birbal showed that he was always loyal to Akbar.

117. *The Widow and the Will*

One day, a widow sought Birbal's help. Her husband had left a strange will. She was not able to understand what it meant. Birbal saw the will. It read: Divide the property among the three daughters equally. None of them should be able to use it. Each daughter should give one thousand gold coins to her mother after receiving her property. The widow enlisted the property and said, "My first daughter is lazy; the second is a miser and the youngest one plays all day." Birbal said, "According to the will, the lazy daughter should be given the village property. The miser should be given a big house and the playful daughter should be given lots of clothes. Thus, all three of them will have what they don't want and will sell them. After selling what they have, they can give you a thousand gold coins each." The woman thanked Birbal and left.

118. *Words of Wisdom*

Emperor Akbar wanted his courtiers to be like Birbal. One day, he said, "Birbal, tell us how wise people should conduct themselves." Birbal began his speech. But he noticed that the courtiers were busy talking to one another. So he fell silent for a few moments. Then he said, "There was a beautiful lady. She was travelling with a parrot and an eel." There was silence across the court. Everyone started listening to Birbal in rapt attention. Birbal continued, "Soon, they reached a river. The parrot flew over the river, while the eel swam across it." Then Birbal resumed his speech on wise people. All the courtiers said, "What about the beautiful lady? How did she cross the river?" Birbal replied, "She was a goddess and will remain so. You want to hear an unnecessary story, but not words of wisdom." Akbar praised Birbal for his presence of mind.

119. *The Donkeys' Fight*

One day, Birbal was on his way home from Emperor Akbar's court. He saw a couple of donkeys fighting. Soon, another donkey came there and tried to interfere. Birbal got off his horse and kept watching the donkeys. When passers-by saw Birbal standing there, they were curious to know why he was looking at the donkeys. They began asking one another, "What is it about the donkeys that has grabbed Birbal's attention?" They continued to gather around Birbal, who paid no attention to them and continued watching the donkeys. One of them asked Birbal, "Why are you looking so keenly at the donkeys?" "I am amazed at the third donkey," said Birbal. "Well, what about it?" asked the man. Birbal replied, "Just like this donkey, humans also interfere in other people's matters without doing their work." People in the crowd understood Birbal was referring to them and soon, they all went away.

120. *The Pink Pouch*

One day, a poor man was walking by the marketplace, when he saw a pink pouch lying on the ground. There were a hundred gold coins in it. Just then, a man shouted, "Has anyone found my pouch? Whoever returns it shall be rewarded." The poor man gave him the pouch. The rich man counted it and was about to leave, when the poor man said, "Sir, where's my reward?" The rich man said, "What reward? You've taken your share. There were two hundred gold coins in my pouch. But now there are a hundred gold coins." The poor man said, "Sir! I am poor, but I am not a thief." Birbal was passing by. He asked, "What happened?" After the rich man had related the incident, Birbal told him, "Your pouch had two hundred gold coins. This pouch isn't yours, since it has only a hundred coins." Birbal gave the pouch to the poor man.

121. *Birbal and the Learned Man*

Once, a learned man went to Akbar's court. Akbar asked, "What brings you here?" The man said, "Your Majesty, with your permission I would like Birbal to test me." Akbar agreed. Birbal brought a huge jar and filled it with big stones. Birbal asked the man, "Can I add something more to this jar?" The man said, "No, it is full." Birbal put pebbles in the jar and shook it lightly. The pebbles rolled into the empty spaces between the stones. Birbal asked, "Can I add something more?" The man said, "No!" Birbal smiled and poured sand into the jar. The sand filled up the empty spaces. Then he said to the man, "This jar is like our life. We feel we have learnt everything and there is nothing more to learn. But there will always be space for more." The man said, "There is no one so wise as Birbal, Your Majesty!"

122. *The Two Friends*

One day, Akbar asked, "Birbal! What is friendship?" Birbal said, "There were two friends named Ali and Sikander. They had a fight and Sikander slapped Ali. Ali felt bad. He wrote in the sand, 'Today my friend slapped me.'" "What happened next?" asked the emperor. "They walked on and reached a lake. They were bathing in the lake, when Ali started to be drowned, but Sikander saved him. Then Ali wrote on a stone, 'Today my friend saved my life.'" Akbar asked, "After Ali had been slapped, he wrote in the sand. But when he was saved by Sikander, he wrote on a stone. Why?" "Your Majesty, Sikander asked Ali the same question. Ali said, 'When someone hurts us, we should write it in sand so that the winds of forgiveness may erase it easily. But when someone does something good, we must write it on stone so that we may always remember it.'"

123. *The Neighbour's Bull*

Birbal had a troublesome neighbour. He was jealous of Birbal and always tried to create problems for him. One day, the neighbour let his bull loose in the same pasture where Birbal's cattle were grazing. The bull killed one of Birbal's oxen. Birbal's servant came running to him and gave him the news. Birbal took his fellow courtiers and went to visit the neighbour. He said, "My bull has killed your ox. Let me repay your loss." The neighbour said, "You are so honest! If you want to repay me, give me one of your oxen in return." Birbal said, "Oh! I am sorry, for I said the wrong words. Your bull killed one of my oxen." The neighbour got angry. He said, "That's impossible. I will not pay you a penny." Birbal said, "You should accept what you wish others to follow." The neighbour paid Birbal and never troubled him again.

124. *The Temple on the Hill*

There was a temple on a hill. The priest of the temple was very old. One day, he passed away. When Akbar heard the news, he sent Birbal to choose the next priest. Birbal stood at the foot of the hill and told the candidates, "Climb up the hill and meet me in the temple within half an hour." The path was steep and full of brambles and rocks. One by one, the candidates reached the temple. Birbal was about to announce the winner, when a wounded man stumbled into the temple. "What took you so long, my friend?" asked Birbal. The man said, "Sir, I was busy removing the rocks and the thorns on the path so that devotees might climb up the hill easily." Birbal said, "Well done! You are the new priest. Anyone can walk on a difficult path. But only selfless people can take care of other people's interests."

125. *A Lesson in the Garden*

One morning, Akbar and Birbal were strolling in the royal garden. Many fruit trees, flowering plants and shrubs grew in the garden. The fragrance of the flowers pervaded the air. Akbar and Birbal were talking to each other and walked into the part of the garden where the gardener was at work. They watched him as he dug a trench around the trees. Then he watered the plants and the trees. He then plucked the weeds that grew all around the garden. Akbar asked Birbal, "The gardener takes care of many plants in the garden. These will wither and die if uncared for. However, there are thrice as many weeds that spring all around the garden even though the gardener doesn't care for them. How is it possible?" Birbal said, "God takes care of the weeds in the garden. But all other plants planted by human hands depend on us for nourishment."

126. *The Thief at the Fair*

One day, Akbar said to his courtiers, "I grant you all a day's holiday to visit the annual fair." Everyone thanked Akbar and left for the fair. Birbal went to the fair along with his family. There, Birbal saw a learned man. The man was actually a thief. He befriended Birbal. Soon, he was awestruck with Birbal's good nature and decided not to rob him. The robber said, "Sir, I am not a learned man. I wanted to rob you." Birbal gave the thief some money. The thief said, "You are good to me even after knowing who I really am! Please offer some advice on life." Birbal said, "Speak only the truth," and he left. The thief was bewildered that Birbal did not ask him to stop robbing. He heeded Birbal's advice. Soon, he gave up robbing as well. Thus, through his wisdom, Birbal helped a thief become a good man.

127. *The Two Brothers*

One day, two brothers stormed into Emperor Akbar's court. Their father had left them his property and they were fighting over it. While the younger brother wanted his share of the property, the elder brother wanted it all for himself. As they continued to quarrel, Birbal intervened. He told Akbar, "Your Majesty, long ago, after God had created the Earth, He created animals and humans. He got so engrossed in creating animals that He had little clay left to create humans. God made humans with the remaining clay, but they were too few. So He turned some of the animals into humans. Although such creations had the body of humans yet they had the soul of animals. Even today, we see some of them." Everybody laughed out loud. The elder brother understood that Birbal was referring to him and stopped quarrelling. Akbar then divided the property equally between the brothers.

128. *The Greedy Monkey*

Once, Akbar, Birbal and all the courtiers went hunting. After a while, they were tired and decided to relax in the shade. They dismounted from their horses and tied them near by. While everyone rested, the soldiers fed peas to the horses. A monkey was sitting on a tree near by, watching the horses. Suddenly, it went towards the horses, grabbed a handful of peas, and climbed up a tree. Akbar and his courtiers watched the monkey. Just then, a pea slipped from the monkey's hand. Greedily, the monkey jumped to catch the pea. While doing so, the rest of the peas slipped from its hand as well. Seeing this, Birbal laughed out loud. Akbar asked, "Birbal, Why did you laugh?" Birbal said, "Sometimes, we act like the monkey, Your Majesty. In our greed for one thing, we lose all that we have." Akbar and the other courtiers laughed heartily.

129. *The Brick of Gold*

There was a miser in Akbar's kingdom. His wife would say, "You are rich, but you never spend a penny. You never give me anything." The miser turned a deaf ear to her complaints. One day, he went to the goldsmith and bought a brick of gold. When he got home, he buried it under a tree in his garden. Every morning, he would wake up and dig out the brick of gold. Then he would bury it again and go about his daily duties. One day, his servant saw him doing this. At night, the servant stole the gold and ran away. Next morning, when the miser found out that the gold was missing, he rushed to Akbar's court and narrated his plight. Birbal advised, "Go home and bury a stone under the tree. Think that it is the gold brick, because when you had it, you never used it."

130. *Stealing from a Thief*

One full-moon night, while Birbal and his family were deep in slumber, a thief entered the house through the window. He took off his shirt and spread it on the floor. He went into the store room and gathered whatever he could. While he was busy, he knocked down a pot. Birbal woke up due to the noise. He tiptoed out of his bedroom and saw the thief's shirt. He understood what was happening. Birbal grabbed the shirt and went back to his bedroom. Soon, the thief put all the stolen goods on the floor and began looking for the ends of the shirt to tie it up. Then he realised that the shirt wasn't there! Just then, Birbal made a loud noise to scare him. The thief realised someone was awake. He left Birbal's belongings and ran away. Birbal shouted, "I shall use your shirt, but next time bring something for my wife!"

131. *The Reading Session*

Once, a budding writer invited Birbal to tea. He had finished writing his first book and wanted to read it out to Birbal. Birbal accepted the invitation. When the writer had read a couple of chapters, Birbal realised it was a badly written book. He wanted to leave. But the writer said, "There's another chapter you must listen to. I'm such a good writer." Birbal did not want to be rude, so he didn't tell the writer what he actually thought about the book. He told the writer that it was getting late, so he must leave. But the writer would not listen. He went on reading. After the reading session, the writer asked, "I shouldn't praise myself, but don't you think I am a great writer?" Birbal said, "Please praise yourself because no one else will!" The writer understood that Birbal wanted him to improve his writing.

132. *The Mango Tree*

One day, Birbal's neighbours, Rashid and Sadeeq, were fighting against each other. He asked them, "What is the matter?" Both of them led him to a mango tree. Sadeeq said, "Birbal, I have nurtured this tree since when it was a sapling. But Rashid says the mangoes belong to him." Rashid said to Birbal, "This tree is mine. All its fruits belong to me." Birbal was silent for a while. Then he said, "Well, both of you are the owners. Pluck the mangoes and divide them between yourselves. Next, cut the tree and divide the wood too." Rashid liked the idea, but Sadeeq cried, "No, Birbal! I cannot cut the tree. Let Rashid have it all to himself." Birbal smiled and said, "Sadeeq, you could not bear to hurt the tree. You win. The tree is yours!" Thus, Birbal showed that we cannot see our loved ones in pain.

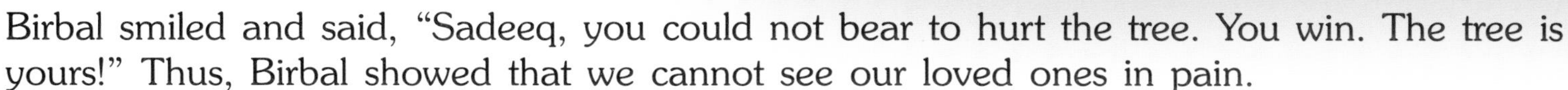

133. *The Quarrelling Neighbours*

Jumman and Imam were Birbal's neighbours. One day, Jumman complained to Akbar that Imam had stolen brinjals from his field. But Imam said, "Your Majesty, I took the brinjals with the permission of Jumman's field. Akbar asked, "Can you explain yourself?" Imam said, "Before plucking a brinjal, I asked, 'O Field! Shall I pluck one brinjal?' The field said, 'Why pluck just one? Take twelve.' So I took a dozen brinjals. The field gave me the brinjals." Birbal whispered in Akbar's ear. Then he said loudly, "Imam, you're right. Come with me." Birbal took him to the royal well. A few guards pushed Imam into the bucket tied to the well and lowered him into it. Birbal asked, "O Well, how many times should I dip him?" "Twelve times!" he said, pretending to hear the well. Imam said, "Please let me go! I'm sorry for stealing the brinjals!" Akbar punished Imam.

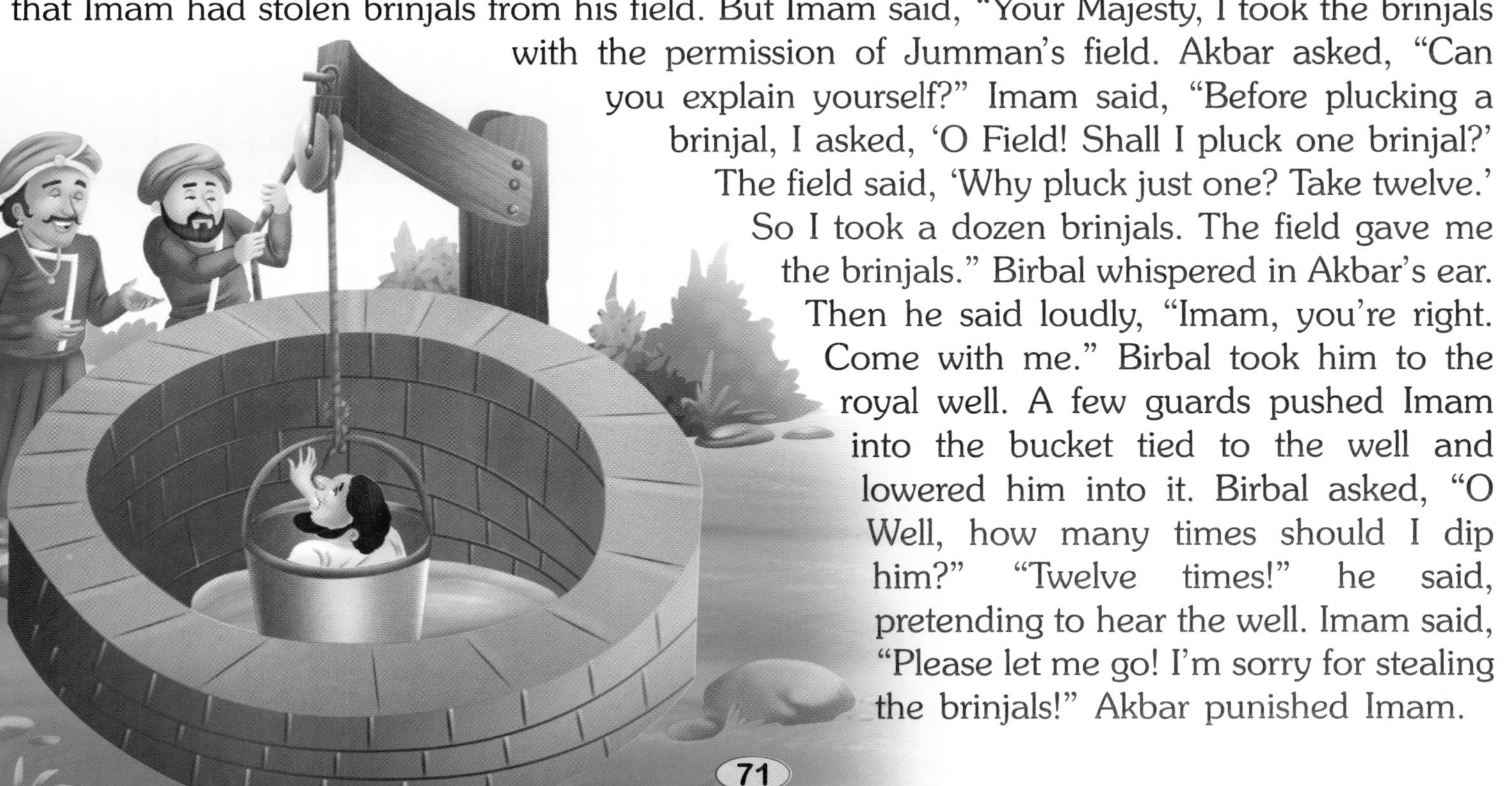

134. *Nothing is Impossible*

One day, Emperor Akbar said to Birbal, "I have a challenge that you cannot face." Surprised, Birbal asked, "What is it, Your Majesty?" Akbar said, "The oldest member of this court is a serious man. Let's see how you bring me his nightwear without asking him to give them to you." Birbal said, "I always love a good challenge!" That night, Birbal put a few red ants in a small jar and secretly went to the courtier's house. When the courtier was about to sleep, Birbal dropped the ants at his feet. The ants bit the courtier all over. He was so vexed that he took off his clothes and threw them aside. Birbal took the clothes and ran away. Next day, Birbal showed the clothes to Akbar. Akbar had a hearty laugh. As he returned the nightwear to the courtier, he said, "Birbal, you win! For you, nothing is impossible!"

135. *The Magic Lamp*

Once, a thief broke into Birbal's house. When Birbal woke up due to the noise, the thief hid in a dark corner behind a lamp. The place was dusty and the thief sneezed. Birbal stood at a distance from the lamp and said, "Dear Lamp, why are you quiet tonight? Is there someone else in this room?" The thief thought, 'If this magic lamp doesn't talk, the man will catch me! I should talk.' So he said, "I hear you, Sir." Birbal said, "How did you go to sleep without listening to a story?" The thief said, "Tell me a story like you do, every day." Birbal said, "There lived an old lady in a village. One night, a thief entered her house. So she screamed, 'There is a thief in my house! Servants, please come in!'" Birbal's servants heard him. They came rushing at once and caught the thief.

136. *The Five Elephants*

Once, Emperor Akbar gave Birbal five elephants. Birbal thanked the emperor and took them home. After some days, Birbal went to the marketplace to sell the elephants. One of Akbar's guards saw this and complained to Akbar. Akbar was angry. He said, "How can he sell the gifts that I have given him?" He took his guards and went to the marketplace where Birbal was. He shouted, "Birbal! You have disrespected me. Why are you selling these elephants?" Birbal bowed and said, "No, Your Majesty, I respect you. I didn't want to hurt you, so I accepted them. I cannot afford to feed such mighty beings at home. I want to sell them and buy five cows. They will give milk and, with each glass that I drink, I will bless you." Akbar calmed down. He ordered his guards to take away the elephants. Then he gifted Birbal five cows instead.

137. *The Lost Woman*

One day, Akbar and Birbal were strolling along the banks of the Yamuna. Suddenly, they heard people shouting. When they went near, they saw some people standing around a man. The man bowed and said, "Your Majesty, my wife left home in the morning to bring water from the river. She has not returned. I am looking for her." One of the men in the crowd said, "I heard a woman shouting for help a while ago. Look for her in the forest near by." Another man said, "Look for her in the market." The man was confused. Birbal said, "If someone heard her shout, she might have fallen into the river. It flows downstream; go there. Hurry up or she will be drowned!" The man jumped into the river and began to swim downstream. He found his wife holding on to the branch of a tree and saved her. They thanked Birbal for his presence of mind.

138. *Never Give up*

A young man was about to jump into a well. Birbal said, "Stop! What's the matter?" The man said, "I wanted to be a farmer but it didn't rain. The crops died. I tried to be a shepherd, but a wolf killed my sheep. I am fed up!" Birbal said, "Come with me!" He took the man to a mahout's house. There, they saw some elephants tied with thin ropes. Birbal told the mahout, "Tie these elephants with a strong chain or they will run away." The mahout said, "When these elephants were babies, I tied their legs with the same ropes and they could not break them. As they grew, they believed these ropes couldn't be broken. So they stopped trying." Birbal told the young man, "Did you hear? The elephants have stopped trying. They don't know their strength. The man said, "Thank you, sir! I will never stop trying!"

139. *Birbal's Secret*

One morning, the topic of discussion in the royal court centred on women and loyalty. But Birbal said, "Women cannot keep secrets, Your Majesty!" Akbar asked, "Can you prove it?" Birbal said, "Give me a week, Your Majesty!" Next day, Birbal pretended to be crying in his room. His wife asked, "Why are you crying, dear?" Birbal said, "Promise me you will not tell anyone that I have laid an egg!" In the afternoon, Birbal's wife told her best friend about the incident and added, "Don't tell anyone!" However, the friend was not able to control herself. She told another friend, "He laid three eggs!" The number of eggs grew with each person. By the end of the week, everyone in Akbar's court knew that Birbal had laid hundred eggs. Birbal's wife apologised to him when she learnt that this was a rumour. Akbar said, "Birbal, you win!"

140. *Birbal Smells a Rat*

One day, a man entered Akbar's court and said, "Your Majesty, I have a special skill. I can train animals to speak like human beings." Akbar asked him, "Can you train my horse?" The man said, "Certainly, Your Majesty! But I need a lot of money. It will take ten years to train your horse." Akbar agreed and said, "Take my horse and the money. But if you fail to train it, I shall punish you!" The man agreed. "Wait, Your Majesty!" Birbal intervened. "This man is asking for a huge sum so that he may live comfortably for the rest of his life. Nobody can guarantee whether the man, you or your horse will live for ten more years. This man is taking advantage of your kindness. Let him train your horse in the palace grounds!" The man said, "Excuse me, Your Majesty!" and he hurriedly walked out of the court.

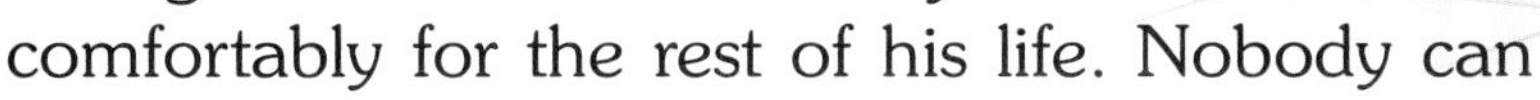

141. *Spilt Tea*

Once, an intelligent man from a faraway country visited Akbar's kingdom. He had heard of Birbal's wisdom and wanted to meet him. Birbal invited the man to his house. They enjoyed discussing many topics. After a while, the man said, "Sir, please offer me a few words of wisdom." Birbal smiled. Then he asked his servant to bring them tea. When the tea arrived, Birbal offered to pour the tea from the teapot. He continued to pour tea even after the cup was full. As a result, the tea began spilling over the rim of the cup, onto the table and ran all over the floor. The man said, "Sir, the cup is already full." Birbal said, "Like this cup, you are full of knowledge. You should use it. Otherwise, it will be wasted, like this tea." The man thanked Birbal. He went back to his country and started teaching children.

142. *The Floating Palace*

One night, Akbar dreamt of a floating palace studded with gemstones. Next day, in the court, he narrated the dream to all his courtiers. He could not forget the dream. Then he thought of playing a prank on his courtiers. He said, “I will give twenty sacks of gold coins to anyone who builds the floating palace for me.” All the courtiers were quiet. For the rest of the day, Akbar kept asking his courtiers about whether they would build the palace for him. But everyone was silent. Next day, Birbal rushed into the court and cried, “Your Majesty! I dreamed that I had lots of money. But someone stole it. I’m ruined!” Akbar said, “It was just a dream, Birbal!” Birbal said, “Your Majesty, if your floating palace is real, my money is real too. The thief should be caught.” Akbar laughed heartily and rewarded Birbal with gold coins.

143. *The Lazy Servant*

One day, Akbar and Birbal were walking in the royal garden, discussing an important issue. Just then, Akbar said, “See, how lazy that servant is! He has been resting under the tree since the time we came here. I will throw him out!” Birbal said, “Please have patience, Your Majesty. I shall turn him into a hard-working person.” Akbar agreed. Birbal walked to the resting servant and said something. The servant got up and started watering the plants. That day onwards, Akbar never saw the servant resting. Many days later, Akbar asked Birbal, “What did you tell that lazy servant? He works so hard nowadays!” Birbal said, “Your Majesty, I told him that you had asked me to promote hard-working servants to the post of royal guards. He is always working hard, as he wants to get promoted first. Akbar laughed and said, “Birbal, you are indeed intelligent!”

144. *The Old Man's Gold*

One day, an old man came to see Akbar. He said, "Your Majesty, my son and daughter-in-law have thrown me out of the house. What shall I do now?" Birbal said, "Your Majesty, I have a plan." Birbal took the old man with him and told him his plan. Then he said, "Go home and try it. See you!" After a few days, the old man went to Akbar and said, "Your Majesty, I am happy now. My children take good care of me after I have followed Birbal's advice!" Akbar asked Birbal, "What was your advice?" "I gave the old man a box of gold coins," Birbal replied. "I asked him to count them when his son and daughter-in-law were looking. He returned my gold coins, but his children think he is rich. They will serve him throughout his life, since they are greedy for his gold!" "Birbal! You are great!" said Akbar.

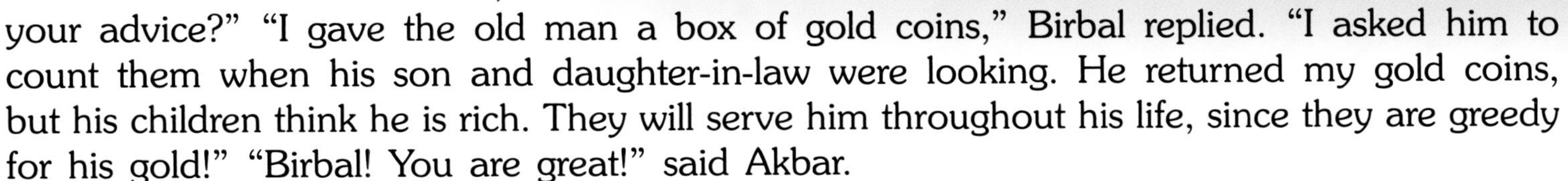

145. *The Dead Sheep and the Broken Wall*

Once, a shepherd and his neighbour came to Akbar's court to resolve their fight. The shepherd said, "Your Majesty, my neighbour's wall fell and my sheep died under it. My neighbour is not paying me for the loss." The neighbour said, "Your Majesty, it's the mason's fault. He did not use quality material to make the wall." The mason was called to the court. He said, "The labourer mixed extra water to the lime! I'm not to blame." When the labourer was questioned, he said, "Your Majesty, the waterman poured more water into the dish." The waterman was called to the court. He said, "The utensil from which I poured the water was really huge, Your Majesty!" Birbal asked, "Where did you get the utensil?" The waterman said, "The shepherd gave it to me!" Birbal said to the shepherd, "You lost your sheep because of your fault!" The shepherd left the court without a word.

146. *Akbar and the Artist*

One day, an artist came to Akbar and said, "Your Majesty, would you like me to paint the likeness of your beautiful palace?" Akbar happily agreed. The artist walked around the palace with his canvas and painted it from every angle. A few days later, the painting was ready. Everyone in the court was impressed with the painting. Akbar gave the artist many gifts. The artist wanted to leave, but Akbar said, "Please stay for a few more days." Next day, the artist told Akbar, "All my belongings have been stolen!" Akbar was furious. But Birbal said, "Your Majesty, I was in doubt, so I sent my servants to find out about the artist. He is actually a spy of our enemy. He has made a map of the palace so that our enemy may attack us." Akbar punished the artist and thanked Birbal for saving his kingdom from great danger.

147. *The Heavenly Rabbit*

One day, a hunter visited Akbar's court. He showed Akbar a strange rabbit and said, "I found this heavenly rabbit in the forest. Please accept my gift." The rabbit had many colours and indeed looked heavenly. Akbar said, "I am happy with your gift. I shall give you a hundred gold coins as a reward." Just then, Birbal said, "Your Majesty, this rabbit looks dirty. It needs to have a bath first." Akbar agreed. Birbal asked a servant to bring a tub of warm water. When he dipped the rabbit in the water, the colours on the rabbit's body washed away. It was just an ordinary white rabbit. Akbar was angry with the hunter. He asked Birbal, "How did you know it's a painted rabbit?" Birbal said, "The hunter used many colours to paint the rabbit and the colour was still present on its nails!" Akbar gave Birbal a hundred gold coins instead.

148. *Weaving Dreams*

Akbar was in a good mood one evening. He decided to tease Birbal. Akbar said, "I had a dream last night. In my dream, I saw you." Birbal said, "Your Majesty, I feel honoured. What else did you see?" Akbar said, "We were walking in the marketplace. It was night. There was darkness all around. Suddenly, we fell into ditches. You fell into a ditch full of garbage. But I was lucky! I fell into a ditch of honey." Akbar winked at Birbal, who understood this was a prank. He quipped, "Your Majesty! Your dream was incomplete." "Why do you say that?" asked Akbar. "I too had the same dream," said Birbal. "We looked for some water to clean ourselves. But we didn't find even a drop. So you licked me and I licked you clean." Akbar had a hearty laugh and said, "You're the smartest of all!"

149. *The Lamp on the Hill*

One day, Birbal said, "Your Majesty, man can do anything for money." Akbar said, "Prove it!" Birbal brought a poor Brahmin and said, "This Brahmin will stand in the icy-cold lake by the hill throughout the night if you reward him." Akbar agreed. The Brahmin stood in the lake all night. In the morning, Akbar asked him, "How did you manage?" The Brahmin said, "A lamp was burning on the hill. I watched it all night." Akbar said, "So the lamp warmed you up. You lose!" Birbal felt sorry for the Brahmin. He did not go to the court for two days. When Akbar visited Birbal's home, he saw Birbal watching a pot of uncooked rice. Akbar shouted, "How can you cook rice without a fire?" Birbal said, "The pot will gain warmth from the lamp on the hill." Akbar realised his mistake. He called the Brahmin and gave him a thousand gold coins.

150. *Sun and Shade*

One day, Akbar was in a bad mood. He scolded Birbal for no reason and asked him to go away. As an obedient courtier, Birbal packed his belongings and went away. After a while, Akbar realised his mistake. But Birbal was nowhere to be found. Akbar knew Birbal couldn't resist a challenge. So he announced, "Anyone who walks in the sun without carrying an umbrella but still is under shade shall win a thousand gold coins." Next day, a man came walking in the sun, without an umbrella. He held a cot made of jute strings over his head and said, "I win! I walked in the sun but was still under the shade of this cot." Akbar knew this was Birbal's idea. He said, "Take me to the man who gave you this idea." The man took him to his house, where Birbal was staying. Akbar apologised to Birbal and took him home.

151. *Guest at the Feast*

Birbal was a keen observer. Once, a merchant invited Birbal to a feast. When he went to the merchant's bungalow, he was surprised to see so many people there. He told the merchant, "There are so many people here! Your house seems like a marketplace!" The merchant said, "All these people are my workers. I have invited only two guests. One of them is you. Can you tell me who the other guest is?" Birbal said to the merchant, "Yes. But first, you will have to tell us a joke." The merchant told a boring joke. When the joke was over, everyone laughed, except a man in a red turban. Birbal pointed towards the man and said, "That's the other guest." The merchant said, "How did you know?" Birbal said, "Your workers always like you, so they laughed even though your joke wasn't good. But the guest was bored. So he did not laugh."